Boat
Electrical
Systems
Dag Pike

GW00536747

Adlard Coles Nautical
London

Published by Adlard Coles Nautical
an imprint of A & C Black (Publishers) Ltd
35 Bedford Row, London WC1R 4JH

Copyright © Dag Pike 1992

First published in Great Britain by
Adlard Coles Nautical 1992

ISBN 0–7136–3451–0

A CIP catalogue record for this book is available from the
British Library.

Typeset in 10/11pt Gill Sans Light by August Filmsetting,
St Helens.

Printed and bound in Great Britain by
J. W. Arrowsmith Ltd., Bristol

CONTENTS

ACKNOWLEDGMENTS

Thanks to Lucas Marine, F Elsenburg Agenturen, VDO, Taplins, Ampair, and BK Electronics for supplying help and photos for the book, and to my secretary Gina Haines for typing and other help.

Other books by Dag Pike

Practical Motor Cruising
Dag Pike takes motor cruiser owners by the hand to show them the ropes of *practical* motorboat handling and management in harbour, on rivers and at sea.

Fast Boats and Rough Seas
A more advanced follow up to *Practical Motor Cruising*, designed to explain advanced handling techniques for fast boats.

Fast Boat Navigation
Aimed at owners of all fast boats from 20 knot cabin cruisers to racing powerboats, fast ferries, patrol boats, lifeboats and sailing catamarans, this book provides a complete survey of the environment and techniques of high speed navigation.

Also available:
Electronics Afloat
Motorsailers

Introduction

Apart from sailing dinghies and rowboats, virtually every boat on the water today uses electricity. Just as it has become essential in homes, offices and motor cars, electricity now plays a vital role in boats. It can bring many of the comforts of home, but more importantly it provides improved safety in the form of powerful navigation lights and electronic systems for safe navigation and emergency use. Of course, it is also vital for starting the engine.

Gone are the days when the electrical system on a boat was a useful thing to have, but it did not matter too much if it failed. Indeed, it seemed like a bonus then when the electrics were working, and because they weren't considered essential one's approach to the system was generally very casual. Today the casual approach to electrics is not just inconvenient; it can be highly dangerous, leading to a failure of essential equipment and even fire.

This book takes you into the world of boat electrics. It will give you a better understanding of the electrical system so that you will treat it with the respect it deserves. It is easy to take the system for granted because it is largely hidden from view, but unlike a house or a car where you can call in the repair engineer if things go wrong, out at sea you are on your own. The book also explains how to create or improve the electrical system to give better reliability, how to check and maintain the system and, perhaps most important of all, what to do if it fails.

To cope with electrics you do need a certain level of knowledge about how they work. The systems may be complex, but if you have a basic understanding you should be able to cope with most eventualities. The majority of electrical problems are fairly straightforward; the complicated side of the system tends to be contained inside replaceable black boxes, so fortunately, even if your knowledge is minimal, this book can still help you to use the system intelligently.

1

The system

Electricity is a strange source of power. You can't see it, but you can certainly see its effects in the form of lights and sparks. It is a very versatile power source in that it can be used in the form of a motor to drive machinery, as a source of easily controllable heat and light, and for powering electrical devices. It can also be used to generate magnetic effects. It is the versatility and convenience of electricity which makes it such a good source of power in a boat.

Electrical systems use metal wires to transport energy from where it is generated to where it is stored and used. The wire has to be insulated in order that the electrical current follows only the chosen path, because any current leaking from the wire or a connection can lead to trouble. Much of the secret of a sound electrical system is in ensuring that the current flows only where you want it to go; in some respects it can be likened to a water supply which is contained within pipes. However, whilst you can see and hear if the water is flowing, electricity is generally silent, making leaks and other problems harder to locate.

One of the major difficulties on a boat is that in addition to being carried by metal, electricity can also be conducted by water. Anyone who has owned a boat knows how damp it can be both inside and out, and the marine environment is a tough one in which to make electrical systems operate satisfactorily. Electricity tends to follow the easiest path – which could well be the route provided by water if it comes into contact with the system. An additional difficulty is that salt water is also very corrosive, so it is important to remember that, in the marine environment electricity and water should not mix. If they do, the water will win, causing a breakdown of the electrical system. Water will not only provide an alternative path for the electric current to follow, but also begin the process of corrosion which, if left without attention, can have serious consequences.

Electricity comes in two forms, direct current (DC) and alternating current (AC). AC is the form we enjoy at home as it is easier to transmit over long distances and offers greater flexibility in the higher voltages needed in the domestic environment. AC motors and generators are also more compact and reliable than DC. With AC current, the power flows in alternate directions many times a second, hence AC power might be described as 240 volts, 50 cycles per second (the number of cycles being the number of times the current changes direction every second).

In boats, AC power suffers from the major disadvantage that it cannot be stored in a battery but has to be supplied on a continuous basis by a generator. On a boat you don't necessarily want a generator running all the time. Moreover, a generator still needs power to start its engine. This means that a battery is needed to store electricity that is available for use when required. The battery will store and produce DC power only, so a boat's electrical system has to be based on this current.

DC power travels in only one direction along a wire which, in terms of the system itself, makes very little difference. It is the ability to store current in a battery which is such a vital element. Not only does this ability enable you to use electrical appliances when the charging system is not operating, it also fulfils the vital engine starting role, which in turn allows the generator to start, so producing current to recharge the battery and supply the onboard systems.

Battery charging

Just to confuse the issue a little further, all modern engines use an alternator to produce electrical current. An alternator produces AC and you might well wonder why AC is produced to power a DC system. The changeover from the DC dynamo to the AC alternator was made because of the alternator's compact size, greater reliability and greater efficiency – particularly when running at lower engine speeds. The alternator was the best way of producing a higher charging current to cope with the increased electrical loads on boats, even though it involved incorporating a rectifier into the charging circuit to convert the AC current into DC. (A rectifier is rather like a one-way valve, allowing the current to flow only in one direction which, of course, is what constitutes DC power.)

The alternator and the battery are two essential parts of a boat's electrical system. The alternator supplies the current which is used to charge the battery, which then supplies power to the rest of the system. When the engine is stopped and the alternator stops charging, the battery takes over the supply role. You may already have spotted the weakness in such a system; if the battery is supplying power to the auxiliary systems throughout the boat and is also required to supply the heavy demands for engine starting so that the alternator can produce more current to recharge the battery, it could happen that there will not be enough power left in the battery to start the engine. This is why modern boats tend to have two separate batteries charged by one alternator; one battery is used to supply the auxiliary systems on board and the other is used solely for engine starting. In this way you should never find yourself in the position of not being able to start the engine.

The alternator is one type of development incorporated into a modern electrical system in order to improve its reliability and versatility. Alternative methods of battery charging have been developed to supplement the alternator supply for this purpose. The alternatives include using a battery charger powered from a shore electrical supply, having an independently powered generator on board which in turn can supply the battery charger, or the use of solar panels or wind powered generators to help keep batteries charged.

Electrical circuits

The basis of a marine electrical system is the charging system and the battery. This is the power supply, but the current now has to be distributed around the boat to where it is needed. There are two parts to this circuit; one for engine starting and the other for the auxiliary requirements. Each circuit is kept separate because the engine starting circuit has to carry very heavy current loadings while the auxiliary circuits have much lower demands.

To cope with the heavy current used by the starter motor, the engine starting circuit uses heavy duty wiring directly connected to the battery. This circuit is controlled by lighter duty wiring through the ignition switch and the starter solenoid, which acts as the switch for the starter motor heavy current. For auxiliary circuits, the power is first taken to a distribution box, from where the power is distributed in individual circuits to the various components of the system. Fuses and/or breakers are invariably fitted to each circuit to give protection should a fault occur in that circuit. This helps to prevent a fault in one circuit affecting the whole system.

Two wires are required to link each component of the system. One, the positive wire, takes the current from the battery to the appliance, whilst the second forms the return link to the battery. If you build up a picture in your mind of this double wire link in the electrical system it will help you to understand what may have happened when a fault occurs.

Only when the circuit is complete will the current flow. A switch is a means of creating a gap in the circuit and preventing the current from flowing. Opening or closing the switch is the way in which the circuit is controlled, but damage to the wiring or corrosion can also open up a gap in the circuit and prevent the flow of current. Alternatively, damage or corrosion could lead to the current leaking away and not following the required path.

One of the main differences between the electrical system in a car and that on a boat is the wiring system. The metal structure of a car and the fact that it is isolated from the road by its rubber tyres means that the body of the car can be used as the return circuit for the wiring, reducing the amount of wiring needed to complete the circuit. On a boat, however, even a steel or aluminium craft, full double wiring circuits are necessary to create a reliable system to prevent current leakage which could cause electrolytic corrosion. The exception to this is the engine, where the engine block usually serves as part of the return circuit for the starter motor and often for the alternator.

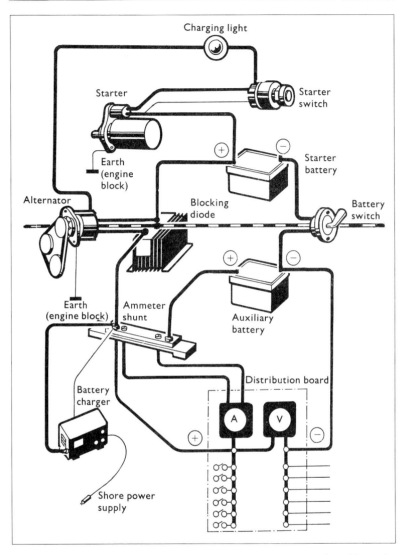

● *The way the electrical circuits are divided into starter and auxiliary circuits. The dotted line shows the division with the alternator, blocking diode and battery switch being common to both circuits.*

Corrosion

Another major difference between car and boat is the corrosive atmosphere of salt water which exists on boats. Many of the metals used in electrical equipment are prone to corrosion in a salt-laden atmosphere, particularly when different metals are used in close prox-

5

imity. A feature of most electrical fixtures and fittings designed for boats is resistance to this type of corrosion.

It can be false economy to use domestic electrical fittings on a boat. Not only can they be more vulnerable to corrosion but there can also be problems over sparking at contacts. This is because DC is more prone than AC to sparking when the circuit is broken, which can shorten the life of AC components which are used to carry DC current.

Reliability

A reliable electrical system is essential on a modern boat and there are no short cuts to a good system. Many factors have to be taken into account, not least of which is the constant movement of the boat at sea. This can be particularly severe on a fast powerboat, but sailboats have violent motions too and the electrical system must be able to cope with this.

Wires must be adequately secured, connections designed so that they will not come loose through vibration, and switches, fuses and breakers designed specially for the marine environment. Some parts of the installation, like the navigation lights, will need to be completely waterproofed. However, it is not just the lights themselves which have to be waterproof, but also the wiring and the connections to complete the system.

By now you will realise that there is a great deal involved in perfecting a boat's electrical system. We will be looking at these different aspects in more detail in later chapters, but it is important at this stage to grasp the fundamental principles of the electrical circuitry on board: the battery is the heart of the system, providing the storage capacity, taking in the charge from the generator and feeding it out to the various consumers of electrical power. Each circuit must have a feed and return wire, and should have a switch and an overload or short circuit protection. Designers and builders of modern boats have come to terms with the requirements of a reliable electrical system so you should not encounter major problems. However, there is a tendency in modern boat building to think 'out of sight, out of mind' – in other words, that electrical wiring which is hidden away does not have to be installed to the same standard as that which is exposed. The reverse is in fact true; in the event of a fault it is the sections you cannot reach easily which need the greatest care.

It is wonderful to enjoy the convenience and safety of an electrical system on board. However, this convenience can only be enjoyed if you can rely on the system; much of this book will be devoted to explaining both how to maintain it in good condition, and what to do if, in spite of this, things go wrong.

2

Batteries – the heart of the system

Let us first look at batteries because they lie at the heart of any electrical system, taking in the power and storing it, and giving it out at the press of a switch to supply the different requirements on a boat. This receiving and dispensing of electrical power is a balancing act so it is important that you don't keep using power without replacing it, otherwise you will find yourself with a flat battery which is neither good for the battery in the long term nor convenient in the short term.

To a large degree this balancing act is controlled automatically, certainly as far as battery charging is concerned. We will look at this in more detail in Chapter 3. Using the power is a different matter, and is largely under your control as equipment is switched on and off. This will be examined in more detail in Chapter 5, but to understand the part played by the battery it is important to understand the balancing act in operation.

Types of battery

There are two types of batteries on boats: alkaline and lead-acid. Although the alkaline battery is now rarely used on boats, it can have advantages in certain applications. These batteries are normally supplied in crates of cells made up in sets to supply 6, 12 or 24 volt systems.

Alkaline or nickel-cadmium batteries have a much longer life than their lead-acid counterparts, but they are more expensive. However, measured over a period of time alkaline batteries could prove economical and, because they can stand idle for long periods without losing their charge, they are better for use in boats, which are often themselves left idle for long periods.

Engine starter batteries where there is a heavy current discharge require a different type of internal construction than those used for domestic loads if they are to give optimum performance. A snag with alkaline batteries is that you cannot measure the state of charge by measuring the specific gravity of the electrolyte (liquid). Apart from this is the high cost – it can be double that of lead-acid batteries – which tends to prevent their widespread use on boats.

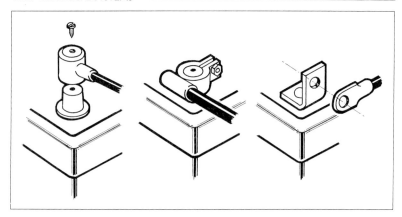

● *Alternative battery connection terminals. The main aim is to get connections over as large an area as possible to handle the heavy duty starter currents.*

Lead-acid batteries

The lead-acid battery is widely used in the marine environment mainly because it is readily available and comparatively inexpensive. These batteries are used in motor cars and trucks, thus the quantity production has helped to keep the cost down and also justified research and development costs which have advanced their qualities in recent years.

Lead-acid batteries are produced in compact units, usually 12 volts for cars, and the high capacity required for boats can be achieved by connecting batteries together in parallel. Better for marine use, however, are heavy duty batteries, produced for trucks, which are more able to withstand the vibration and movement on the sea. They can also provide the higher capacity needed to supply domestic loads on a boat when the engine is not running (and thus not replacing the power being taken out of the battery). Many manufacturers market special marine batteries which are designed to cope with this type of usage, but they tend to be more expensive. This could be justified by a longer life, of course, but in general the truck-type battery is adequate.

The latest development in lead-acid batteries is the sealed, low maintenance unit. Again, originally designed for road vehicles the attraction of these batteries is implied in the name; virtually no maintenance and no chance of spillage. However, it pays to remember that these batteries are designed for road vehicles where the pattern of use of electricity can be very different from that on a boat. The starter battery may have a similar function, but the boat battery can have long periods of discharge when no charge is being put back, and this so-called 'deep cycle' pattern of charge/discharge is not very kind to the sealed battery.

If a sealed battery is reduced to 40 per cent or less of its full charge –

something which could easily happen on a night passage in a yacht or during a night at anchor in a power boat – then neither the alternator nor a conventional battery charger will be able to bring the battery back to full charge. It will need special charging equipment which may not be available at the harbour side.

There is the worry that if the battery is charged at a higher than normal voltage, as could happen with some chargers, it will give off gas at a higher than normal rate and this will not be reabsorbed as would be the case normally. The result will be excessive pressure in the battery, causing the relief vent to blow with a consequent loss of electrolyte which cannot be replaced by topping up.

Sealed batteries are adequate for use on sports boats and similar craft which tend to have the engine running for most of the time the boat is in use, and for applications where the battery is kept topped up by a charger when the engine is not running. Otherwise the most suitable type is the heavy duty lead-acid battery.

Battery loads and capacity

It is quite easy to calculate the nature of loads which may be placed on the battery so that you can work out the size or rather the capacity of battery you require. If you are likely to use the boat for, say, 24 hours when the battery is not being charged, you need to calculate what the load may be and fit a battery of at least 25 per cent more capacity so that there will be little chance of it being run down completely.

For a sailboat this load should be calculated for when at sea, whilst for a powerboat you should calculate for when it is in harbour or at anchor, for that is when the engine will not be running. To make this calculation you need to know two basic formulae:

$$\text{Amps} = \frac{\text{Watts}}{\text{Volts}} \text{ and Watts} = \text{Amps} \times \text{Volts}$$

For most electrical equipment power consumption is given in watts or sometimes amps (or amperes). In order to calculate the battery capacity required you need to translate the watts into amps (watts divided by voltage). For any boat the voltage will be constant at 12 or 24 volts. Amps is the measure of electrical power, and once you know the amps consumed by each item of equipment you can work out approximately how many hours it will be used during the 24 hour period. So if a navigation light is rated at 6 watts, this will equate to 0.5 amps (dividing the 6 by 12 for a 12 volt system). If the navigation light is likely to be on for 10 hours, simply multiply 0.5 by 10 to give a total of 5 amp/hours of power required from the battery during the 24 hour period in question. A similar calculation for each piece of electrical equipment on board will give you the total amp/hours from which to estimate the required battery capacity.

Of course the figures will vary from boat to boat, but the following is an example for a powerboat in harbour:

Lighting	6 lights at 1 amp each
Water pump	1 at 5 amps
Refrigerator	1 at 10 amps
Radio/TV	1 at 3 amps
Fan	1 at 3 amps

Now you have to estimate how often each item will be switched on during the 24 hours; this could be 6 hours for the lights, 1 hour for the water pump, 6 hours for the refrigerator (remember it is not actually using power all the time), 2 hours for the TV, and 3 hours for the fan. From this you can calculate the ampere hours by multiplying the amps by the time used, so we have:

Lighting	6 amps for 6 hours = 36 ampere hours
Water pump	5 amps for 1 hour = 5 ampere hours
Refrigerator	6 amps for 6 hours = 36 ampere hours
Radio/TV	3 amps for 2 hours = 6 ampere hours
Fan	3 amps for 3 hours = 9 ampere hours

which gives a total of 92 ampere hours.

You obviously need a reserve too, so that at the end of the 24 hour period the battery is not completely flat.

A 150 ampere/hour battery should do the job comfortably.

On a sailing boat at sea, without charging the battery you would have to alter the figures to include navigation lights and electronics, but you may not have the refrigerator or water pump, so the total could be similar.

On a powerboat at sea there could be higher loads still, with windscreen wipers and items like radar and searchlights to be added, but then with the engines running and the batteries being charged, there should be no problem with them keeping up with demand. However, it would pay to determine total likely consumption at sea and compare this with the output from the alternator; if consumption is higher than output, then there could be a steady drain on the batteries.

The balancing act performed by the batteries can be measured by an ammeter. This indicates whether the input from the charging systems is higher or lower than the output and gives a constant check on how the battery charge is faring. What the ammeter does not show is the state of battery charge, ie how much power is left. For this the best indication is a voltmeter, because as the battery loses power the voltage drops, so you will receive some warning before the lights dim. There will be more on this and how to connect ammeters and voltmeters in Chapter 5.

The best plan is to fit the largest battery you can comfortably accommodate in order to have adequate reserves. On performance boats, of course, there has to be a compromise between battery capacity and weight, because the additional weight of heavy batteries could detract from the boat's performance.

Battery stowage

It can not be emphasised too strongly how important it is to install the batteries both thoughtfully and securely. You will need access for servicing, and the stowage should allow the batteries to be removed with ease. Batteries can also be dangerous in that they can give off highly flammable gases, and they can be a fire hazard if the large capacity cables start moving and cause a short circuit. Finally, just to convince you of the need for care, the electrolyte is corrosive and can be a particular danger on metal boats.

One of the sad factors about battery stowage is that the position is only decided after the engines and other equipment have been allocated their space. But batteries should come higher up on the list of priorities for several reasons. First, the heavy duty cable running between the battery and the engine starter motor should be as short as possible, both to avoid the voltage drop which can occur with the heavy flow of current, and to reduce the chance of damage to these cables which are not protected by fuses or breakers. Damage in the cable could quickly lead to a short circuit, and cause a fire from sparking or overheating.

Secondly, it is necessary to consider what lies above the proposed position of the battery. When being charged, lead-acid batteries give off hydrogen gas. This is highly flammable or explosive so it is not wise to have pockets of it collecting where it might be ignited by a spark. Since hydrogen is lighter than air, it invariably will rise and disperse quite naturally. It is only when the battery is under heavy charge that dangerous quantities of hydrogen are given off, so you will need to take extra care to ensure there is adequate ventilation if the battery is being charged by external means or from a low charge condition.

Problems due to hydrogen build up could occur if the batteries have been charged with the engine hatches shut; the air intake system wouldn't clear the gas naturally. Open the hatches and let any gas disperse before pressing the starter button. Above large banks of batteries a gas-proof electric fan with a suitable outlet is sometimes installed to clear the hydrogen, but this is really only necessary when the batteries are stowed in a small compartment. Do not put electrical equipment which might spark above the batteries.

You will want the batteries to be easily accessible for checking the state of charge with a hydrometer, and so that you can top them up with distilled water if required. This requires top access – something not always easy to achieve on a boat. In addition to easy top access you also want to protect the top of the battery from the possibility of dripping water, and from someone working on the engine putting down tools where they could create a major short circuit across the terminals. Modern batteries protect most of the connections between the individual cells, but the two terminals still need protection.

Water can easily drip on to the battery, of course, when the engine hatch is opened; with the battery often close to the edge of the hatch it

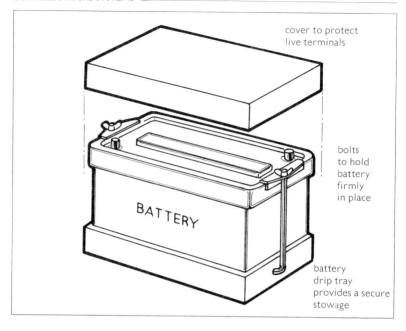

cover to protect
live terminals

bolts
to hold
battery
firmly
in place

BATTERY

battery
drip tray
provides a secure
stowage

● *A securely stowed battery with protective cover.*

can easily get wet. Even with the hatch shut water can drip down, and this water (or even dampness) can cause at best a slow loss of charge as the current slowly leaks between the positive and negative terminals, and at worst a rapid discharge of the battery. Corrosion will also occur at the terminals, which can create its own problems, so keep water well away from the batteries.

Now for the actual stowage itself. I have seen numerous batteries stowed in a tray or a box on board – a good idea, because if the tray or box is properly constructed so that it does not leak and is lined with GRP or lead, then any spilt battery acid will not attack the boat's structure. However, unless the battery is firmly secured in the box or tray itself, this could create a problem. This can come from two different sources. Firstly the loose stowage of a battery in a tray or box assumes that the boat is going to stay reasonably upright. Sailboats can be laid over on their beam ends in a sudden squall and a powerboat can take a sudden jump when meeting an unexpected larger than normal wave. In either of these situations you probably have enough trouble without the additional problems of a heavy battery roaming loose in the boat, wires short circuiting, possibly with a fire risk, and electrics going dead.

I recall the case of a steel fishing boat in which the battery was simply tied down with rope. Chafe eventually caused the rope to break, creating a short circuit with the battery cables, which in turn started a fuel fire. The crew had time to think about battery stowage when they were sitting in the life raft awaiting rescue. In another case the steering wire broke in a boat with wire and pulley steering. The steering was put out of action – not in itself a serious problem, but in breaking, the wire fell across the battery terminals short circuiting the battery, and started a fire; we only rescued the crew when the stern of the boat was burnt virtually to the waterline. A strong case for protecting the top of the battery.

It is worth taking trouble with battery stowage and making sure it is firmly bolted down. Lashings and any type of stowage which allows even a small degree of movement is not adequate because eventually the movement will increase, with the main battery cables being the first to give way under the constant movement.

The heat of the engine room is not kind to batteries either. When the temperature is around 60°F batteries lose their charge at the rate of about one per cent per day when left standing and not charged. At the higher temperatures found in the engine compartment the loss will be much greater, although when these higher temperatures are being created the engine is running and charging the battery. However, the same conditions which create a greater loss from the battery also make it less efficient at higher temperatures, so try to avoid them.

Finally, batteries should be mounted as high as possible inside the hull. The main reason for this is that if you are unfortunate enough to have a leak (and it could be simply an engine cooling water pipe which fails) then the bottom of the engine compartment will fill with water, probably before you even become aware of the problem. If the battery is situated here and gets flooded, you immediately lose the power for the electric bilge pump to help keep the water under control whilst you try to find the leak. If that doesn't convince you to keep the batteries out of the bilges, then remember that your radio also works off the batteries; if you can't solve the initial problem, you won't be able to call for help either if the battery is under water.

So where should you stow the batteries? A popular place is on the forward bulkhead of the engine compartment. This can give good accessibility, but it is far from ideal in other respects; the batteries will be low down, there is electrical equipment in the vicinity which could cause sparks, and the batteries could be exposed to water dripping. However, located here the cables to the starter motor do have a short run. On sailboats where the battery is often alongside the engine the cable run can be even shorter.

A better stowage is in a locker placed on the opposite side of the engine bulkhead. This adds very little extra to the cable run yet it isolates the batteries from the vibration and heat of the engine compartment. In such a position the batteries are generally readily available for maintenance or removal, but the locker must be well ventilated and there should be no switches or relays mounted in the same locker which might cause sparks. You will also need to consider

● *Here the batteries are located low down in the engine compartment, the ropes do not secure the batteries adequately, the wiring is not secured to prevent movement and there is no cover over the batteries or the terminals. It will work, but will not give reliable performance.*

what other items you put in the locker, particularly metal items which might make contact with the battery terminals and cause a short circuit.

There is no simple solution to battery stowage, and in general you will be stuck with what you have. However, it is usually possible to improve on existing stowage by fitting covers or protection and by securing batteries properly. Both will go a long way to providing the sort of reliability you need.

12 or 24 volts?

Boat electrical systems generally operate on 12 or 24 volts DC. There are benefits for each voltage, but in reality you won't have a lot of choice because the decision will already have been made with the engine installed in the boat. In general, petrol engines tend to be 12 volts and diesel engines 24 volts, the difference being determined by the high power needed to crank a diesel engine. If we return to the Watts = Amps × Volts formula we can see that if we use a 24 volt system, then to get the same power (ie watts) we need half the amps compared with a 12 volt system. It is the amps which decide the size of wire and size of motor, so with a 24 volt system, the starter motor needed for diesel engines still remains fairly compact even though it is producing greater power. The wires from the battery are also a reasonable size with a 24 volt system, even though they are carrying greater power. The trend in Europe is towards 24 volts for all engines, whilst the USA tends to remain with the 12 volt system. The difference reflects the shore supply voltage in the respective areas, which is 10 times the battery voltage used in each case.

Whilst the engine manufacturer decides on the voltage for the engine mounted equipment (ie alternator, starter motor and instruments) the owner has a choice as to how the battery installation is carried out. Batteries are made up from multiples of cells, each producing 2.2 volts DC in fully charged form. These cells are made up into groups which can produce either a nominal 6 volts or a nominal 12 volts; 24 volt batteries are rare. If your boat has a 24 volt system then you have the choice of linking four 6 volt batteries together or two 12 volt batteries to get the required voltage. Similarly, with a 12 volt system you have the choice of one 12 volt battery or two 6 volt units. Grouping the batteries in this way does give some flexibility in the way they can be installed.

A 12 volt system tends to be less expensive in most respects, probably because it is widely used in cars. However, it does require heavier duty wiring because of the higher amperage currents it has to carry to do the same job compared with a 24 volt system.

Watts are a measure of electrical power, so if you have a piece of equipment which consumes 48 watts, then on the 12 volt system this will use 4 amps, whilst on a 24 volt system it will require 2 amps. It is the amperage which causes wires to overheat if they are too small, and which demands large motors for a given wattage. Whilst the 12 volt system is quite acceptable in boats, the future trend is towards 24 volts which tends to give greater efficiency and reliability. To change from one system to the other is very expensive and entails changing all the electrical equipment on the engine, so you are really stuck with what you already have on board. However, if you have a 24 volt system and you have set your heart on fitting a piece of equipment which is only available at 12 volts, do not despair. A low powered (say, less than one amp) feed could be taken from a 12 volt section of a 24 volt battery bank without harm. It must be properly wired in and the circuits covered by fuses or breakers. You may want to do this if you have US electronic equipment which you want to install in a European boat.

Connecting batteries

It would seem logical to have a single battery to provide all the electrical power. Connections are always a weak point in any electrical system, and a car has only a single battery. However, as we have seen, the battery requirements on a boat differ greatly from those on a car, and if a single battery were used to supply all the power requirements and provide a reserve, it would be too heavy to handle easily. You should bear in mind that there will be times when the battery has to be removed from the boat, so the maximum weight of any battery should not exceed 80 lbs.

A six volt battery with a capacity of 200 ampere hours – typical of the capacity required for boat use – will weigh around 80 lbs. A 12 volt battery with a similar capacity will weigh almost double, making it extremely difficult to handle within the confines of a boat. The logical

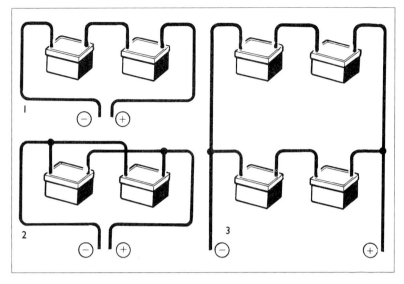

● *Different methods of connecting batteries.*
1 Batteries connected in series to double the voltage
2 Batteries connected in parallel to double the capacity
3 A combination which will double both the capacity and the voltage

solution here is to install two 6 volt batteries which will give greater flexibility in how they can be stowed – side by side or end to end. With a single battery this choice is removed. With a 24 volt system you have little option but to fit multiple batteries, but here the choice is between four 6 volt batteries or two 12 volt units. Again, weight considerations will be the main factor.

There are two different ways in which batteries can be connected; in series or in parallel. The method used will depend mainly on which voltage of batteries you have and what you require the voltage and ampere hours of the total installation to be. Connecting batteries in series means that the positive terminal of one battery is connected to the negative terminal of the next. You can go on adding batteries to the chain in this way, with the final output being taken from the free terminals at each end of the chain. This type of connection is used to increase the voltage output, so that if you have four 6 volt batteries connected in series the output voltage will be 24 volts. This is the best system if you want to use smaller batteries but need to produce a higher voltage.

Connecting batteries in parallel has the opposite effect. With this type of connection the voltage will remain constant, but the capacity (ampere hours) will increase. To connect batteries in parallel, the positive terminal of one battery is connected to the positive terminal of the next, and the same with the negative terminals. The output connections can be made at any convenient point along the positive and negative connections.

Of course it is also possible to link a bank of batteries in a combination of series and parallel connections. Some of the batteries are linked in series to increase the voltage and some in parallel to increase the capacity. The best way to arrange this is to make the parallel connections first to create a package of larger 6 volt units, and connect these in series to increase the voltage output. In this way, four 6 volt batteries could be connected in series to produce 24 volts, giving a high capacity at a manageable weight. When linking batteries in either series or parallel, heavy duty wires are necessary.

This demonstrates how batteries can be connected to produce the capacity and voltage required, but more important is the way in which batteries can be connected into the system so that one can be reserved solely for engine starting whilst a second is used to supply the auxiliary requirements throughout the boat. Such systems are now commonplace, particularly in powerboats; they offer security by ensuring that the engine starting battery will remain fully charged, or close to fully charged, whatever the state of charge of the auxiliary.

Another benefit of such a system is that the auxiliary circuits are not subjected to the voltage drop which can occur when the heavy starter motor current is drawn from the battery. For lights and most other electrical equipment this voltage drop is not a problem since there will be just a temporary interruption in the supply, but for navigation equipment the voltage drop caused by engine starting can cause a position fixing receiver or a radar set to switch off completely, and it will have to be reset before it can be used again – a nuisance if it happens just before you set off to sea.

We will look more closely at these twin charging, double battery systems in Chapter 3, but connections to the battery outlets are made in a normal way; one battery is linked to the engine starter motor via the solenoid switch, which in turn is connected via the ignition switch, and the other is linked to the auxiliary supply distribution box. The common charging link to the two is split by means of a blocking diode, each battery having its own diode which acts like a one-way valve in the system. It allows the current to flow from the alternator to the batteries, but not to flow back to the alternator nor to flow from one battery to the other.

Battery switches

There may be occasions when you want to link one battery to another. Such a connection is often incorporated into the starting circuits by means of a special position on the battery switch. This allows the reserves of two batteries to be combined, which might be just enough to provide power to turn a starter motor when one battery won't do the job. This would be a requirement mainly on a twin engined boat without the blocking diode charging system and with only a single

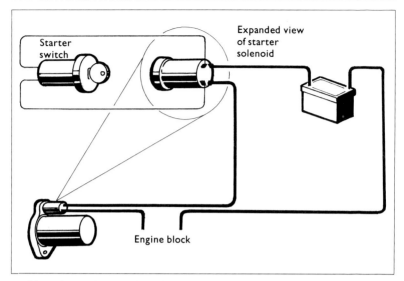

Starter switch

Expanded view of starter solenoid

Engine block

● *How the engine starting circuits are connected, with the starter solenoid acting as a relay to switch the powerful starting current.*

battery on each engine to supply starting and auxiliary needs. The heavy duty switch used to temporarily connect the two batteries is called a paralleling switch; it effectively connects both starter batteries in parallel so enabling the combined capacity of the two batteries to supply starting current. It probably won't help much if both are nearly exhausted, but is a great help if one has been run down and avoids the need to rig jump leads between batteries.

Each battery should also have an isolating switch. This is a heavy duty switch which, like the paralleling switch, should be capable of carrying the full starter motor load. The isolating switch should be as close to the battery as possible. It fills a safety role as well as providing a means of reducing battery drainage. The safety aspect comes from isolating the circuits from the battery, so that any fault which occurs when the boat is left unattended will not result in a short circuit. By isolating the battery from the circuits, there is also a greatly reduced chance of current leakage because of damp atmosphere or bad insulation.

Never, never switch off the isolating switch whilst the engine is running as this will create an open circuit in the alternator. This in turn will create a high voltage surge, which will almost certainly damage the regulating and rectifying diodes in the alternator, and the only solution will be a replacement alternator.

Jump leads or booster cables

Despite modern electrical systems, the risk of a flat battery still remains, particularly on smaller boats where twin battery systems are not justified. Coping with a flat battery at sea is very difficult, if not

● *An isolator or blocking diode which allows two batteries to be charged from the same alternator.*

impossible, as you cannot conjure up a charging current if the only way of providing it is through an engine which cannot be started. There is the possibility of using jump leads from another boat, and these also provide a viable means of starting the engine in harbour when the battery is flat. If a trailer boat's battery is flat the towing vehicle's battery could be used for engine starting.

Using jump leads for engine starting on a boat requires care. Remember that hydrogen gas can collect above the battery, and connecting the jump leads can cause sparking. Firstly, make sure that the engine of the craft or car from which the power is being taken is stopped. Then check that there are no faults in the cables or their connectors, because a heavy current will be flowing through them. Next, connect the positive terminals of the two batteries, making the connection to the receiving battery first. After that it is the turn of the negative cable, which should be connected first to the negative terminal of the donating battery and then to the negative terminal of the

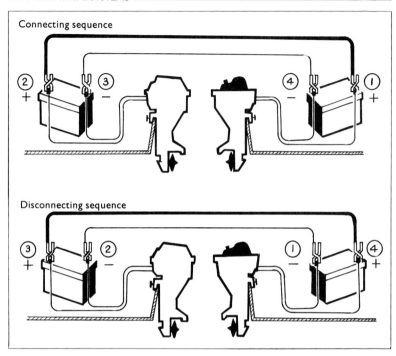

● *The sequence for connecting and disconnecting jump leads. The boat with non-functioning batteries is on the right. The top diagram shows the connecting sequence and the bottom that for disconnecting.*

receiving battery. Sparks will be generated when making the final connection, so it is safer to make this connection to the engine block if this is used as part of the earth return, rather than to the battery itself, as it reduces the risk of igniting any gas which may be present.

After checking all the connections, start the engine relating to the donating battery and then attempt to start the engine of the receiving battery. In this way first the engine will continue to run even if a great deal of the power is taken out of its battery. Once both engines are up and running, disconnect the cables in the reverse order, ie the positive connection last, making sure that you do not accidentally make any short circuits whilst doing so.

Care and maintenance

We will be looking at this aspect in detail in Chapter 7, but the need to devote the necessary care and maintenance to the battery cannot be overemphasised. It is the heart of your electrical system, and if the battery fails, so will much of the equipment you take for granted. This equipment is there both for your safety and convenience, so do not leave the battery to its own devices until the first signs of weakness show in an engine that is reluctant to turn over. It is very easy to keep batteries out of sight and out of mind – which is one very good reason for installing them where they are easily visible and where you can see the first signs of any corrosion or a falling level of electrolyte.

Battery Dos and Don'ts

- *Take care that you don't make a wrong connection to the battery charger.*

- *Never use a battery tester whilst the battery is being charged.*

- *Connect first the positive terminal of the battery.*

- *Switch off the charger before disconnecting from the battery.*

- *Disconnect first the negative or ground side of the battery.*

- *Make sure that all battery connections are tight and secure.*

3

Generating power

Just as important as the batteries themselves are the means of generating power to keep the system supplied. The primary means is the engine driven alternator, but it is not the sole means. Smaller amounts of power can be generated by solar panels, wind and water generators, and even by using wave energy. Finally there are battery chargers which can be used where shore power is available, or when they can be connected to an on board independent generator which supplies shore power voltages. This wide choice can be confusing and it is a case of looking at each method to identify the system or combination best suited to your particular boat and the way you use it.

Engine driven generators

There are two main types of engine driven generator, the dynamo and the alternator. It may surprise you to know that both produce alternating current, so the output has to be rectified into direct current before it can be fed to the battery, which will only accept DC current. The dynamo was the standard form of generator before the advent of solid state electronics; the alternating current produced in the rotating armature windings is rectified into direct current by the electro-mechanical action of the carbon brushes on the segmented commutator.

In the alternator the output is generated in the fixed field windings, so that the expensive and wear-prone commutator is not required to pick up the generated current. From the field windings the alternating current is passed through a rectifier, which uses diodes to allow the current to pass in only one direction. As we have already noted, a diode is like a one-way valve and will only pass current in one direction. This not only transforms the alternating current into direct current, it also prevents the electrical current stored in the battery from flowing back through the alternator when the engine is stopped.

With a dynamo, where the current is picked up from the commutator, there is no such one-way valve in the system, so an electro-mechanical cut-out has to be installed. This is a solenoid relay which is activated when current starts to flow from the dynamo; the contacts close and the current can flow to the battery. When the dynamo stops, the contacts open and the path for any reverse flow back through the battery is broken.

The alternator has replaced the dynamo on all modern engines for a number of reasons. The commutator is a source of wear, and brushes need maintenance, and although the alternator has brushes, they operate on continuous slip rings rather than the segmented commutator, so they are virtually maintenance free. The alternator is also less sensitive to the speed at which it operates, and a big bonus is that it can produce charging current at useful levels even when the engine is running at idling speeds. Most alternators are self limiting in current output and require only a voltage control, but perhaps the main reasons why they have been so widely adopted is that they are maintenance free and cost less than an equivalent dynamo.

An idea of the flexibility offered by the use of an engine-driven alternator is that a typical unit will start to generate power at around 1000 revolutions per minute (rpm), and by the time it is rotating at 3000 rpm the power output will have risen to 47 amps. The power output climbs steeply in this speed band and then levels off, so that at 5000 rpm it will have reached its maximum output of 55 amps. However this is not the end of the story, because this unit will go on producing power up to its maximum safe speed of 10 000 rpm. In assessing these figures you have to remember that the ratio of the drive pulleys for the alternator is around 2:1 for a petrol engine and 3:1 for a slower running diesel engine, so the alternator will cut in and produce around 20 amps even at engine idling speeds and still operate safely at maximum engine rpm.

An output of 55 amps will match the average running loads of most smaller powerboats, but where a wide range of electrical equipment such as radar and powerful radio telephones is installed as well as comprehensive domestic appliances, then an alternator with a higher output may be required. Certainly the alternator output should comfortably exceed the current being used under normal circumstances, so that the batteries will be topped up to replace the power used when the engines are not running. It is possible to fit larger alternators in place of the standard unit in many cases, but you would need to check with the engine or alternator manufacturer, bearing in mind that a larger alternator would need more power to drive it, which in turn might require a stronger driving belt or even a double belt drive.

Alternatively you could fit a larger alternator driven by a separate power take off from the front of the engine. This might be a free standing alternator mounted on a separate bed plate, but this is only viable when the engine is solidly mounted, otherwise the movement of the engine on its flexible mounts would vary the tension in the alternator drive belt, which could cause belt slippage and/or rapid wear.

Rather than change to a new, larger alternator, a better alternative might be to install a second alternator mounted on the engine and driven by a separate drive belt. This second alternator would need to be mounted on a specially constructed bracket with built in adjustment for the drive belt, but it has the positive advantage that any failure in one alternator still leaves you with a charging system, even

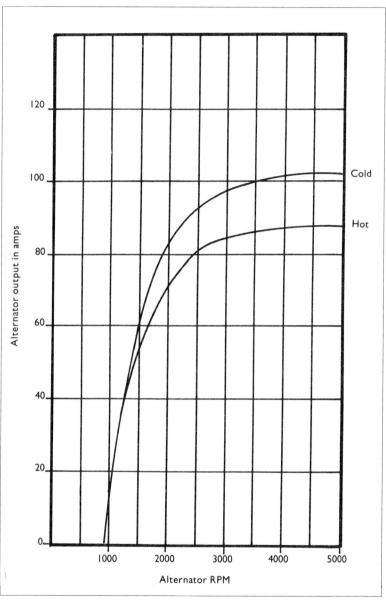

● *Typical alternator output wires showing how the output rises rapidly.*
Remember that the alternator usually runs at least twice engine speed, so it
could be producing 40 amps at idling speed.

though this will be at a lower rate. If two alternators are used they are
connected in parallel, and the rectifying diodes incorporated will prevent currents flowing from one alternator to the other.

Regulators

An alternator is capable of sending a heavy charging current to the batteries, but when they are fully charged this heavy current will only lead to gassing from the batteries which will, in the longer term, cause them damage. To prevent this happening a regulator which automatically cuts back the alternator output when the battery is fully charged is introduced into the charging circuits. (A similar system was used with dynamo charging, using an electro-mechanical regulator, but the modern regulator used with alternators is a solid state sealed unit.)

Most regulators used with alternators work by sensing the battery voltage and reducing the flow of current from the alternator when the voltage reaches a certain level. The voltage is a good indicator of the state of charge of a battery. When it drops below 11.4 volts on a 12 volt battery, the battery will need a full rate of charge because it has reached the state when further discharge could do damage.

The normal charging voltage from the alternator will be around 14 volts for a 12 volt system. This higher voltage is necessary in order to ensure that the current flows into the battery and not the other way round. If the charging voltage rises to 14.4 volts, the battery will start gassing, so the regulator has the delicate job of maintaining a high charge rate when the battery voltage is low and then reducing the current flow to a trickle when full charge is reached.

The problem is complicated in that the voltage of a fully charged battery is 12.7 volts when it is not being charged or used. This would be the ideal measurement to take, but it is not possible to do so when the battery is being charged because the terminals will only show the voltage of the current from the alternator (which, of course, is higher). The regulator, despite its sophistication, is still a fairly crude instrument for controlling the flow of current to the battery, and some manufacturers have produced secondary regulators which incorporate electrical circuitry aimed at controlling the alternator output in a much more subtle way to reflect the charge state of the battery. These are connected in parallel to the existing regulator and are intended to cope particularly with large banks of batteries or those which have been deeply discharged. These secondary regulators are claimed to do a better job than the standard unit, although alternator manufacturers do not yet specify them. However, secondary regulators are comparatively new to the market and it can take time for major manufacturers to catch up with innovations, so these units are worth exploring if the use pattern of your battery is such that it can become heavily discharged.

Double battery systems

We looked at the benefits of twin battery systems, one reserved for engine starting and one for auxiliary requirements, in the last chapter. There are several ways in which these benefits can be obtained by using manual switching and automatic blocking diode systems. The

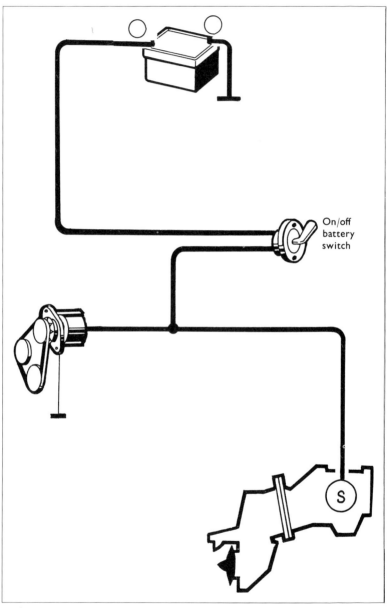

On/off
battery
switch

S

● *Single battery and single alternator.*

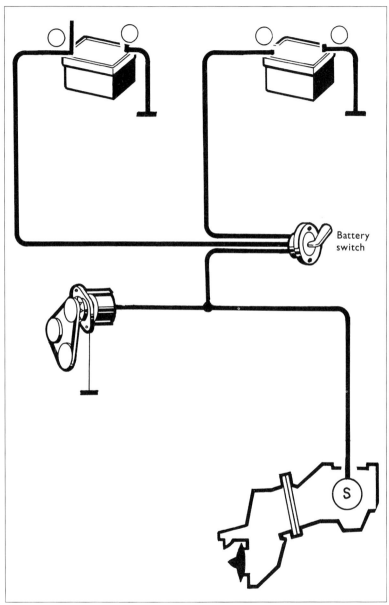

● *Twin battery and single alternator using the battery switch to manually select the battery to receive charge and to supply the circuits.*

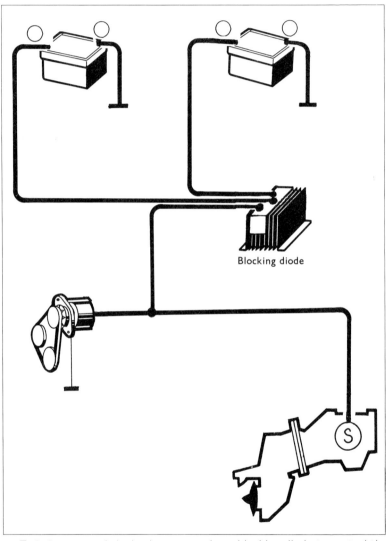

Blocking diode

● *Twin battery and single alternator using a blocking diode to control the charging of the two batteries.*

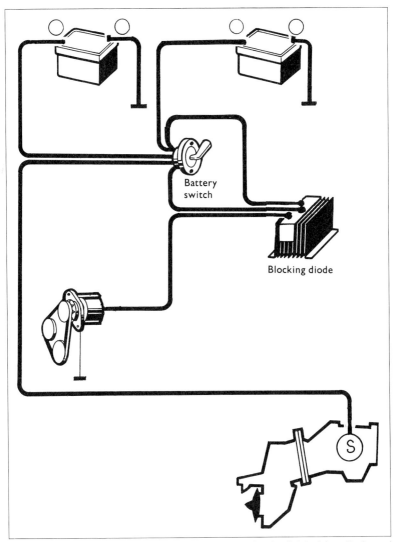

● *Twin battery and single alternator incorporating both blocking diode and battery switch.*

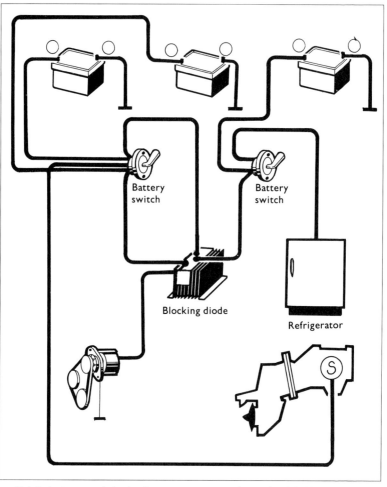

● *Triple battery and single alternator system where the third battery is used to supply the refrigerator.*

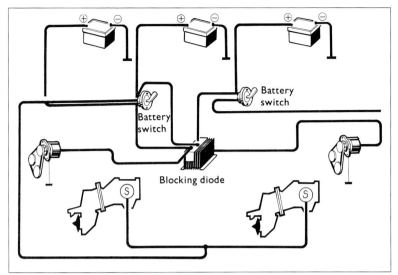

● *Triple battery and twin alternator system typical of that found on many modern powerboats.*

diagrams on pages 26 to 31 show how the different systems can work, so that you can choose one to match the precise needs of your boat.

The simplest case is a single engine charging a single battery with an isolating switch in between. This is the type of arrangement which could be found on a small sports boat or sail boat where the auxiliary requirements are small and there is little risk of exhausting the battery. A step up from this type of installation is to have two batteries instead of one to give extra security for engine starting. In the simplest arrangement, these batteries can be linked by a manual switch which allows the charge from the alternator and the starting and auxiliary requirements to be switched from one battery to the other. The battery being charged is the one being used to supply power; with this system both batteries cannot be charged at the same time. The manual switch should allow contact with the second battery before disconnecting the first, so that the circuit through the alternator is not open.

If the manual switch is replaced by a blocking diode you can charge both batteries at the same time; one can be reserved for starting and the other for auxiliary use, which is obviously a better arrangement. The battery with the lowest charge will be charged first. It is possible to have different sizes of battery with this system, although they must be of the same voltage. A manual switch incorporated into the battery circuit can allow the roles of the batteries to be changed and can also allow them to be paralleled for emergency engine starting. This is a good system, catering for most contingencies and is the one generally installed on single engine boats today.

There is a further refinement of the system which is sometimes employed when an item of equipment such as a refrigerator places a continuous demand on the battery supply, and could exhaust the auxiliary battery and all the circuits it feeds. This alternative uses three batteries. The batteries for engine starting and auxiliary use are connected as previously, but a third battery is connected into a triple outlet blocking diode solely for supplying the refrigerator. This means that all the other electrical instruments on board can continue to be used even if the refrigerator drains its own battery.

With a twin engine installation you can, of course, employ any of the above systems, keeping the system for each engine totally separate. Certainly you want to have separate starting batteries for each engine, with the possibility of paralleling them, and if there were two auxiliary batteries one could be used for the refrigerator and one for the remaining auxiliaries. Alternatively you could divide the auxiliaries into essential and non-essential items, and operate each group from a separate battery. There is a lot to be said for having two separate and independent battery and charging systems, but in the interests of economy many boats now use a three battery system, two for engine starting and one for auxiliary use.

For the latter arrangement the alternators from each engine are linked in parallel into the blocking diode. From the diode the charging circuits are linked to all three batteries so that the one with the lowest charge has priority for charging. Either starting battery can be selected through a manual switch, allowing either engine to be started from either battery. Of course, paralleling is also possible between the two starting batteries. The auxiliary battery has its own isolating switch and, apart from charging, operates on a separate circuit from the other two batteries.

With all these different systems available the choice is wide. In order to select the best system you need to identify the electrical requirements on your boat, and the level of redundancy or safety you want to build in to guard against failure. There is something to be said for having as many batteries as possible in case of failure, but batteries are heavy and expensive so it is rare to find a boat with more than three banks of batteries.

In addition to engine powered charging systems there is a variety of alternative power sources which can be coupled in to complement or replace the engine systems. These can all offer advantages in certain circumstances, but as with batteries it does not pay to get too complicated. We'll look at some of these now.

Solar power

The idea of getting something for nothing is always appealing and this is the attraction of solar panels. They generate an electrical current when exposed, not just to the sun, but in any kind of daylight. Although the current is small, it is very useful in providing a trickle charge to keep the batteries fully charged when the boat is left unattended.

Solar panels consist of a series of photovoltaic cells linked together and protected between rigid or semi-rigid panels, the top panel being clear glass or plastic to allow the light to reach the cells beneath. The semi-rigid panels are better for boat use because the surfaces to which they have to be fastened are rarely flat.

A 2 sq ft panel will produce about 6 watts of power in bright sunlight – not very much, so a panel of this size is only suitable for keeping a small battery topped up. Larger panels will obviously produce more power, but if space doesn't allow a single larger panel, the small panels can be linked in parallel to increase the power output. Most panels on the market today are rated at 12 volts, so if your boat has a 24 volt system, then two panels should be linked in series to obtain the required voltage. In dull conditions the output will be halved.

One of the snags with solar power is that it produces most power when you are least likely to need it. Its role then is primarily to keep batteries topped up. However, an installation of larger panels could be useful on a sailboat to provide power, through a battery, for electronic navigation equipment. Portable panels are available which can be rigged on deck as required, but a permanent installation is much better and modern units are rugged enough for deck mounting.

Connecting solar panels is a simple matter. If there is more than one panel, take the leads from the panels to a junction box, and from there the twin leads can be taken to the charging system. The wires could be connected directly to the battery or alternatively to the alternator side of the battery isolator/selector switch, which would allow the current to be directed to either battery. Solar panels have a diode incorporated so there is no worry about current feeding back through the panels from the battery. Since the panels are in effect directly linked to the battery, even though the isolator switch may be off, the leads from the panels could be a source of short circuits unless the wiring is carried out to the highest standards. Because they are left unattended, the portable panels could pose an unacceptable risk, particularly if they are connected to the battery terminals by spring clips. A useful safety feature would be to fit a fuse into the supply leads to give some protection against faults; this fuse should be as close as possible to the battery on the positive side.

Wind and water generators

Wind generators are another free source of electric power, but you have to put up with the rather unsightly and possibly dangerous propeller whirling around above your head. Wind generators have the advantage that they will operate both night and day, and a typical unit will produce 4 amps in 20 knots of wind for a 12 volt system. This is fine for replacing current used in domestic or navigational activities, but is too high for just topping up the batteries when the boat is unattended.

For the latter application you would need a regulator to control the output in relation to the battery voltage, just as you would with the engine driven alternator.

Two types of propeller are used for wind generators, one is a conventional propeller with five or six blades, and the other a vertical propeller or turbine. The latter takes up less space and is less visually intrusive, but it is also less efficient, and much will depend on how or where you want to mount the unit. The conventional propeller type is really only suitable for stern mounting, clear of sails and rigging, and it needs space to rotate around its vertical axis to keep it facing into the wind. The vertical propeller, by contrast, could be mounted on the mast.

The alternator of the wind generator is usually contained within the hub of the unit and is fitted with diodes to rectify the current and prevent feedback as with the engine alternator. These units are installed mainly on sailboats where they can provide power both at sea and in harbour. They are adequate for modest needs, probably enough to keep navigation lights and electronics operational.

Water generators use much the same sort of alternator although it is packaged to be mounted on the stern and driven by a towed or fixed propeller. The towed version is something like the old style towed log, with a tow rope linking the propeller to the transom-mounted alternator. The fixed type is more like an outboard motor mounted on the transom. The underwater hub contains the alternator which is driven by a propeller on the horizontal shaft. The electrical connections are taken through the tube which supports the underwater unit. Once again designed mainly for sailboats, these units provide power only when the boat is moving through the water, and are designed to meet only modest requirements. Output at 6 knots could be around 5 amps at 12 volts, but of course the performance does depend on the speed of the boat.

Connections for both wind and water generators are the same as for the solar panels, and feedback protection is incorporated. With both systems you get power both day and night, but when it is calm you get nothing. A price has to be paid with both systems in terms of reduced boat performance, but in most cases the difference will be negligible.

Shaft generators

A shaft generator is one which has a driving system linked to the boat's propeller shaft. In its simplest form there is a drive pulley on the propeller shaft which links to the pulley on the generator shaft. Shaft generators can perform in two different ways.

Firstly it can act like a water generator, with the propeller turning due to the forward motion of the boat and thus driving the generator. Such a system could be used on a sailboat to produce electrical current when the boat is under sail, but it is not as efficient as the dedicated water generator, and the gearbox does need a suitable arrangement

● *A water powered alternator with towed propeller. The black propeller unit connects and turns the alternator by means of the rope by which it is towed.*

whereby it is lubricated when the output shaft is turning without any input from the engine.

Secondly, shaft generators can be used to generate a 120 or 240 volt supply on a powered craft to avoid having to run them as well as the main engines. We will look at such systems in Chapter 4 because they are used more for these higher voltages. However, there is nothing to stop you rigging a shaft generator for 12 or 24 volts, and it can be a comparatively inexpensive way of obtaining extra power – but you have to remember to disconnect it when manoeuvring, and on a small boat it is not a good idea to have electrical installation down in the bilges where they can be vulnerable to water. An extra alternator on the engine would be a better way of obtaining the power you need.

Battery chargers

As a power source for charging the battery, a charger has a lot to commend it. However, like most things connected with the electrical system on boats, there are right types and wrong types, and different methods of using them. The basic principle of the battery charger is quite simple; the mains supply of electricity at 110 or 240 volts is converted by transformer into a 12 or 24 volt supply, which of course is still AC at this stage. This current is then passed through a rectifier which converts the AC into DC, to give a supply which is suitable for charging batteries.

The rectifier in the charger will act as a stop to prevent current flowing back through the charger from the battery when the charger is not in use. This means that the battery charger can be installed permanently in the boat and the mains power supply connected when charging is required. The mains supply itself should also be a permanent installation to avoid any risks with the high voltage current. This is only practical when the boat is equipped with a shore supply system which is plugged in when the boat is in harbour. Flexible leads could be used to power the battery charger if a shore supply is not installed, but be particularly careful with such leads especially if they get wet in rain.

Using a portable charger should only be considered as a temporary expedient to restore a flat battery in an emergency. The charger itself is probably quite safe, but the risks come from the leads from the charger to the battery and the spring clips used to make connection with the battery. The risks are from sparking and short circuits on these leads and you could end up with a battery flatter than you bargained for if something does go wrong, this quite apart from the risk of fire. When connecting the charger leads to the battery, always connect the negative lead first and then the positive, and always disconnect the negative lead before the positive. This reduces the risk of short circuits. Do not switch on the charger until all the connections have been made, and switch off before disconnecting to reduce the risk of sparking.

The normal car type battery charger is not usually suitable for boats except when it is being used in a portable capacity. Any battery charger fitted on a permanent basis should be constructed to resist the corrosive marine atmosphere if it is to have a safe and useful life. Chargers are rarely waterproof, and there is little need for this, so install the charger high up in the hull, well clear of the bilges and clear of any drips. Battery chargers generate heat as well, so ensure that air can circulate around them.

● *A battery charger installed on a yacht. It is plugged into the mains supply, and because it gives off heat the notice warns to allow air circulation.*

The battery charger you use should incorporate a regulator because, just like the alternator, the charging current needs to be cut back to a trickle once the battery is fully charged. The charger should also incorporate a fuse on the positive side of the charging circuit; the high voltage side of the system will be protected by the fuse in the shore power supply system. The charger can be connected directly to a battery. For general harbour use this will be the auxiliary because the starting batteries will not need charging unless the boat has lain idle for some time.

You can use the battery charger supply to the auxiliary battery as a direct means of power supply, with the battery doing its normal balancing act. Obviously you won't want to keep taking out more than you put in, so the battery charger should be rated to match the normal load needed in harbour. This could be quite low if you use shore power

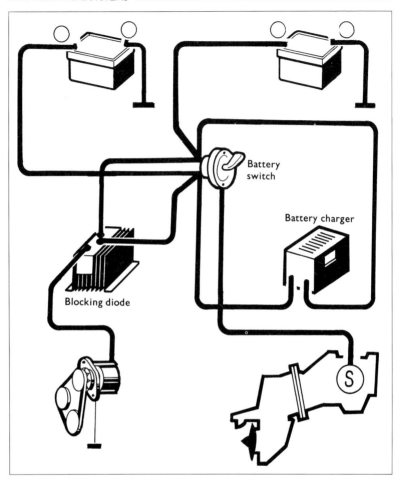

● *How a battery charger is connected into the charging circuits. The shore power supply to the charger is not shown.*

to supply many of your power requirements in harbour. Compact battery chargers operating from the shore supply can be obtained in ratings extending from 5 to 50 amps, so there should be no problem in finding one to meet your requirements. Make sure that the shore supply is adequate to handle the load of larger chargers, however. And if you plan to charge two batteries through the blocking diode, check that the charger is suitable for this type of use.

Precautions with generators

Once properly installed a generator should give long years of useful life. Apart from the drive belt from the engine, virtually no maintenance is needed, and the system will run automatically. The weak point on the generating side of the installation is the battery which will slowly deteriorate, but a good and efficient charging system can do much to prolong its life.

The charging system should be matched to the way the boat is used. If it is used intermittently you will need some other form of charging in addition to the engine driven generator to keep the battery topped up. This could be a wind generator or solar panels, or if there is access to a shore power supply, then a battery charger could be your answer. On a sailboat the problem of maintaining power supplies is more difficult, and unless when you are at sea you want to run the engine to charge the batteries you should seriously consider the back up of wind or water generators or solar panels, particularly for long cruises. Even a powerboat could find wind generators useful if a lot of time is spent at anchor, and for all craft there is always the option of a small portable generator to produce both 12 or 24 volt DC power as well as limited amounts of higher voltage power. This is perhaps the most flexible alternative, and avoids having to take the uneconomic step of running the main engines. Such generators can be obtained in both petrol or diesel form to give fuel compatibility to the host craft. If you use a portable generator at sea make sure that it is well secured and that the portable leads do not come into contact with hot surfaces or get nipped.

It is when you are making alterations to the electrical system, or taking batteries ashore, or otherwise working on the charging system, that you are likely to cause faults. Left alone the system will generally be very reliable, but if the alternator is disconnected when it is running (either by switching off at the isolating switch or as a result of a battery or other terminal coming loose) then the alternator is likely to be irreparably damaged by the sudden high current surge which will flow through it. The same can happen if the polarity of the battery is reversed either by connecting the wrong terminals or by connecting a second battery incorrectly as could happen when using jump leads.

It is possible to guard against both these occurrences. For the first you can fit a surge voltage limiting device across the main alternator terminals. This acts as a short circuit when the surge reaches a certain level and protects the vulnerable diodes inside. To protect against reverse polarity a fast fuse inserted between the battery and the alternator will blow before the current reaches danger level. These are not normal fittings in a charging circuit, and are only really necessary if you are forgetful or careless, but they could be useful if different people who are not familiar with the systems use the boat.

The diodes and transistors used in both the alternator and the regulator are voltage sensitive so don't try checking these units with an insulation (Megga) tester which puts a high voltage current through the system. Nor should you run the engine with the alternator leads disconnected as this can cause glazing of the slip rings inside. If you have to use the engine then take the drive belt off. These are rare and unlikely problems, but it pays to be aware of them if you want the charging system to have a long useful life.

On many installations it can be confusing when you try to identify the wiring of the charging system. You might follow the wiring from the alternator and find that it goes to the starter motor solenoid rather than to the battery itself. You could jump to the conclusion that the alternator and the starter are in the same circuit when, despite the connection, they are quite separate. The reason for this is quite simple: the connection from the alternator to the starter solenoid is purely a convenient way of linking the alternator to the battery because the main battery lead also comes to the solenoid. It is done this way simply to shorten the wiring. An alternative could be to take the alternator leads to the battery switch. It can be confusing when you try to trace leads but you simply have to look a little further than the obvious to see what else is connected to the same terminal.

4

Shore power and generators

Chapter 3 ended by showing how there can be a link between shore power and the battery system; now it's time to look at shore power in more detail. With the growth in the number of berths, shore supplies of electricity are more readily available and boat builders are responding by installing shore power connections and circuits into boats as a standard feature. There are obvious benefits in terms of bringing all the comforts of home on board, but there are considerable dangers if the system is poorly installed.

As previously mentioned, electricity and water should not mix, and if they do water will always win. With battery powered systems, if water gets to any connections or fittings then the worst that can happen is that you have an inoperative system and a flat battery. With shore supply voltages the risks from water are much greater. The voltages used can be lethal, so a sound installation and care in its use are vital.

The concept of having mains voltage on board opens up the possibility of enjoying all the comforts of home – freezers, electric cookers, electric kettles, microwave ovens, washing machines, water heaters and television. Some of these can be enjoyed by using 12 or 24 volt systems (refrigerators, television and microwave ovens, for example) but unless the battery is being charged they can cause quite a heavy drain, which can exhaust the battery fairly rapidly. For equipment with heavier power requirements such as cookers and water heaters, there is no question of using the battery even when it is being charged because neither the battery nor the charging system would cope.

The advantage of shore power lies mainly in its higher voltage. The wattage of the equipment is the determining factor; the following table gives some idea of the wattage of various items of equipment:

Cooker	6000 watts
Microwave oven	1000 watts
Refrigerator	500 watts
Water heater	3000 watts
Hair dryer	1000 watts

We noted in Chapter 2 that Watts = Amps x Volts, and so if we have a 3000 watt water heater operating on 240 volts, this will require 12.5 amps. On 110 volts it will need just over twice that amount, but if you tried to operate the water heater on 24 volts you would need a massive 125 amps – a load which would drain the battery in under an hour and which would require heavy duty wiring the size of the starter motor

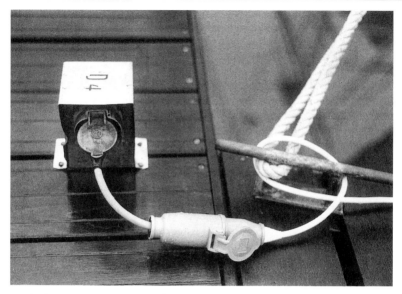

● *A shore power connector in a marina. Here a short length of additional connector allows the cable to be plugged in if there is a different socket on the dockside.*

cables. Using 240 volts the load is acceptable and the cable size reasonable, so if you want the full home comforts on board, then either 240 or 115 volts is the route to follow. There are three ways of getting this voltage on board.

Shore supply

This the easiest method because all you need is a suitable cable connected to a power point on the shore. The snag with such a system is, of course, that you can't take it with you when you go to sea, but for many people this is acceptable; they simply fit dual voltage refrigerators and microwave ovens to overcome the lack of high voltage at sea, and temporarily forgo the use of high power users like the cooker and water heater. On powerboats you can retain the use of the water heater by having a water tank which can be heated by either the shore electricity supply or from the engine cooling system. Shore power is fine so long as you operate from the same berth all the time or know that you can find a plug-in point when cruising. There is now increasing standardisation of marina power points, so that connection is easier when away from home, but going abroad can bring its problems with different sockets and different voltages.

The cable linking the boat to the shore needs to be rugged to stand up to the treatment and exposure it will receive and the current it will have to carry. It is possible to use a domestic wandering lead if it has suitable plugs and sockets, but this casual approach to high voltage

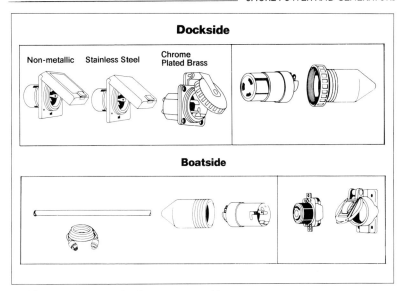

Dockside

Non-metallic   Stainless Steel   Chrome Plated Brass

Boatside

● *The components of a shore power cable.*

electricity will get you into trouble sooner or later. It also means leaving a hatch or porthole open to bring the cable on board, so you won't want to leave the lead connected when the boat is unattended. The open hatch or port will also be a nuisance in rain and possibly a danger if water runs down the lead and into the connection box.

There is a strong move towards the standardisation of power supply sockets both on boats and at the shore connection so that you can plug in wherever you are. However, different countries still have different approaches to plugs and sockets although the US 60 amp push and twist plug with flat pins is becoming the standard. In Britain BS 4343/16 amps and BS 4343/32 amps are still common and are quite suitable for the lower rated power supplies which are often all that is available at marinas. The US type plugs and sockets can handle higher ratings, and although designed for 110 volts are adequate for 240 volt supplies.

Shore power cables should never have live pins. This means that the end of the cable you connect into your boat will be a socket, with the fixture on board being a plug. This may seem back to front, but the last thing you want is live pins on a plug exposed where you might touch them. Even though they are protected from rain, the connections at each end of shore supply cables should be waterproof to reduce the chance of corrosion and the risk of water running down the cable on to the connection.

The shore power cable should be adequate, and well protected, for the current it has to carry. For a 16 amp current a 2.5 sq mm wire is adequate and for 32 amps, 4 sq mm. Heavy duty insulation will protect the cable where it might be trodden on – on the marina pontoons – and the cable should be long enough so that with movement of the boat at the berth it is not inadvertently used as a mooring line. You can make it just the right size for your regular berth, but if you cruise a lot then a longer cable, say up to 25 metres, will enable you to connect up at most marinas where a supply is available. To cope with different types of connection you should take alternative plugs with you for the shore end of the cable you connect into your boat will be a socket, with the directly into the shore end of your cable.

The location of the shore power connection on board is important. This should not be inside because you don't want to leave hatches or ports open, but even though it is a waterproof connection it will benefit from being protected. On some boats it is fitted in a small locker in the cockpit, or in the transom where stern-to mooring is common. Otherwise it is located in a semi-protected position in the cockpit. If the connection is in the open, then it should be angled downwards so that water will not run down the cable and into the connection.

Generators

A more flexible way of producing the higher shore power voltages is to have a generator on board. With a generator you are completely independent and can have the use of electrically powered equipment both at sea and in harbour. To avoid having to run the generator all the time, a common arrangement is to have an installation which can be connected to the shore supply when in harbour and which can be powered by the generator when at sea or away from your home port where a shore supply may not be available. A changeover switch enables the onboard circuits to be fed from either power source and prevents feed back from one to the other.

Modern generators are mainly diesel powered, although the guiding rule here should be to use the same fuel as the main engine. Diesel generators tend to be noisier and produce more vibration than their petrol counterparts, but are more economical and last longer. However, noise and vibration can be critical with generators, because whilst you may be happy to put up with engine noise at sea, the noise of a generator running whilst stationary can disturb a quiet anchorage or upset your neighbours in a marina.

The problem of noise and vibration means that particular care has to be taken when installing the generator. Locating it as far as possible from the accommodation will help, but the engine compartment is often under the saloon or the cockpit, which are the prime social areas on board. The normal engine compartment insulation will not absorb the noise, so it is common practice to enclose the generator in a sound box to help damp out the noise. This box can turn the generator into quite a large package, so unless it has been designed into the boat it can be very difficult to find adequate space for a retrofit. The generator will need servicing just like the main engines, so leave space for access to all parts.

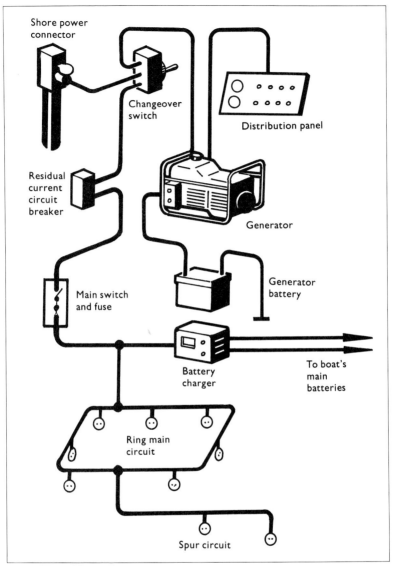

● *The components of a short supply circuit with an on board generator incorporated.*

The generator should be flexibly mounted to reduce vibration, which involves introducing flexible sections into all the connections such as fuel lines and exhaust. The exhaust is a difficult area for generators; it is generally taken outside the boat to reduce the onboard noise, but it can prove offensive to neighbours who have to suffer it. Silencers can help keep the noise levels down. Another alternative is to have the option of switching the exhaust to alternative outlets so that it can be directed away from neighbouring craft.

Generators tend to be taken for granted, particularly when they are shut up in a soundproof box. Monitoring of their operation tends to be casual, so it is a sensible precaution to fit them with alarms governing water temperature, oil pressure and rpm, so that you will receive warning before the engine has major problems. Keep the generator self-contained as far as possible, including a separate fuel feed from the tank and its own starter battery. The installation should be up to the same standards as the main engines. Since the generator could be left running when there is no one on board, an automatic shut down system should be considered if any of the monitored parameters such as pressure or temperature changes, so as to avoid expensive damage to the unit.

The size of the generator is decided in much the same way as for the DC battery system. Add up the wattage of all the equipment on board and this will give you the top consumption – and remember that there isn't a battery in the system to compensate for any temporary extra loading. Generators are normally rated in kilowatts (kW), with one kilowatt being 1000 watts. You are unlikely to have every device switched on at once, so you can probably accept a generator with a rating less than the total, but not too small otherwise you will have to go round switching equipment off before you can switch something else on, or the generator will shut down because it is overloaded.

Another reason for having a higher rated generator is that it will be better equipped to handle changes of loading. When you switch on new equipment, particularly with a high wattage, there can be a drop in voltage as the generator struggles to cope with the extra load. This is bound to be more of a problem with a smaller generator working near to capacity than a larger one. This extra loading can also be a problem where the unit being switched on has a powerful electric motor. With an air conditioner, for example, when the motor cuts in the initial loading can be two or three times the normal running load, and this extra consumption could be enough to make the generator cut out if it is working to near capacity.

As far as generator controls are concerned there are two main options, manual or automatic start. With manual start you have to activate the starter switch just like starting the main engines. With automatic start, sensors detect when a switch has been closed and automatically respond by starting the generator. This adds to the convenience of the system, but could result in the generator starting at night when a light is switched on, to the annoyance of everyone on board. Manual starting is to be preferred in that you will check the output voltage and running of the unit at start up.

All modern generators produce AC, and all high voltage equipment used on board will operate on AC. This is the same power as used at home; indeed much of the equipment like hair dryers, television sets, microwave ovens and refrigerators will be identical to your home appliances. AC is current which switches back and forth and it does this at a certain number of cycles per second, normally 60. This cycling rate is carefully controlled on shore at the generating station, but on board it is unlikely that the generator will be able to produce the same accurate number of cycles per second, which explains why some equipment like electric clocks and some types of tape and record player will not operate satisfactorily on board when a generator is providing the power. This matching of the cycles of AC is one of the reasons why shore power and on board generated power cannot be mixed in the same circuits. It is almost impossible to get the match perfect, and major damage could result.

Another point to watch with alternating current is the way the current flow switches from one way to the other. All shore supplies and generators will have what is termed a sine wave curve, which means that there is a gradual switch in the flow of each cycle. From a peak in one direction, the flow diminishes and then steadily builds up in the other direction. The alternative is the square wave flow, where there is a sudden transition from one direction to the other. This square wave current is produced by some convertors of DC to AC, which we will examine later. Some equipment will not operate happily on square wave AC, mainly equipment such as microwave ovens, television sets, computers and electronically controlled battery chargers.

Alternative production of AC power

Generators and shore supply are the main methods of obtaining AC power on board, but there are other methods. You could run a high voltage alternator from the main engine by belt drive, but this is not entirely satisfactory because the alternator needs a constant speed to maintain the correct number of cycles per second. Special drive systems are available which keep the alternator at constant speed when the engine speed varies, but the cost of these can only be justified on larger vessels.

Another option to drive an alternator is a hydraulic drive. This system uses a hydraulic pump driven by the main engine, with the alternator driven by a hydraulic motor. This system allows the alternator to be mounted remote from the engine and makes the hydraulic power available for other uses, but in harbour it does mean keeping one of the main engines running to obtain the AC current. It can be a useful system at sea on a motor boat where shore power can be connected when the boat is in harbour.

The other two alternative systems convert power from the battery from DC into AC. This immediately limits their use to power equipment with a comparatively low consumption, otherwise the drain on the battery would be too high. The rotary convertor is a unit in which a DC-powered electric motor drives an AC alternator. In practice the motor and generator are combined on the same shaft, sometimes using the same armature to improve efficiency.

The invertor is a solid state appliance which makes the conversion from DC to AC electronically. Whilst the power output of a rotary convertor is limited only by its size and the tolerance of the battery drain, an invertor tends to be more limited in capacity; probably the maximum output you could hope to achieve is around 1 kW, although most are much less.

Neither rotary convertors nor invertors are particularly efficient. Both produce heat which is wasted energy, and the maximum efficiency is likely to be around 80 per cent. This would be achievable with a square wave invertor; a sine wave unit would have a lower efficiency. The low outputs and comparatively low efficiency thus make invertors suitable only as a temporary means of making AC available, perhaps to power an electric drill or for a television set, but not for any permanent long term use such as powering a refrigerator.

Finally, there are the portable types of generator using an air cooled petrol or diesel engine. These are very useful units to have on board, but they do need adequate ventilation, so finding a suitable location where the generator can be kept dry is not always easy. Most have a plug-in socket for the power output and they can usually produce mains voltage AC or battery charging DC from separate windings on the generator. They are not particularly quiet, and their main purpose is for repair work when using electric tools or for temporary battery charging rather than for constant use.

Obtaining power through any of these alternative systems is not cheap. The low efficiency of the invertor raises the cost of engine generated DC power being used, whilst the fuel costs of a portable petrol-engined charger can be up to ten times the cost of similar power from the mains supply. Even a diesel generator can be three or four times the cost of shore power, even without considering the capital costs involved, so the shore cable connection is the option to go for if possible.

High voltage circuits

There are differences between the low and high voltage circuits on board. Whilst both need an outward and return wire to each appliance being supplied, one of the main differences with high voltage is the need for a third earthing wire to ensure safety. With 12 or 24 volts any short circuit in the equipment will lead to rapid failure and blowing of the fuse, but with higher voltages it may lead to the equipment becoming live, which could have fatal consequences if it is not earthed. The earth wire provides an escape route for the leaking current, which will cause the fuse or breaker to blow and will not leave the equipment live and able to give you an electric shock.

Because high voltage circuits are equivalent to the electricity supply in a house, you need to follow much the same wiring and safety procedures. The current will be taken from the shore connection point to the main distribution board which is normally located inside the cabin, in a dry place away from opening windows or doors where water could enter. Between the shore supply socket and the distribution board, and usually mounted on the board itself, are two important safety devices. The first, and most important, is a fuse or circuit breaker which is designed to break the circuit if the current coming into the boat exceeds the capacity of the on board system. We will be looking at the role of fuses and circuit breakers in more detail in Chapter 5, but the main reason why they would blow is if there was a short circuit which caused a sudden increase in the electrical load. The same could happen if more appliances were connected than the system could supply power to, so these fuses or circuit breakers also prevent the wiring being overloaded.

With the three wire system used for high voltages, the live wire and a second wire (called the neutral wire) carry the current, whilst the third is the earth wire. There should be no current flowing through the latter, whilst the current flowing through the other two should be equal. The second safety device is a residual current circuit breaker (RCCB) which compares the current flowing between the live and the neutral wires. If it is the same, then all is well and no current is leaking to earth, but if there is a difference, then it means more current is coming into the boat than is being used, so it is leaking to earth somewhere, possibly through one of the crew who has touched a live connection. The RCCB is normally set to break the circuit if the difference between the live and neutral wires is more than 30 milliamps and this can literally be a lifesaver.

To give maximum protection these two safety devices should be as close as possible to the shore connection plug. The shorter the wires, the less unprotected cable there is. Much the same applies if a generator is installed on board, except that here these safety devices are usually installed in the control panel mounted on the generator itself.

The earth wire is an important safety feature of these high voltage circuits. With shore supply the earth connection is taken ashore through the cable and is earthed ashore, but with a generator it has to be earthed to the generator itself, which in turn has to be earthed to the water outside, either through the stern gear or via a separate earthing plate on the hull underwater. Of course, on a steel or aluminium boat the earth can simply be connected to the hull, but for wooden or GRP craft proper earthing is necessary. Where both shore supply and a generator are installed, then a changeover switch between the two is necessary. This switch should break one circuit before it connects the other, and there is usually an 'off' position between the two 'on' positions. This switch should be placed in the circuit before the main fuse and RCCB, unless the generator has these safety devices incorporated, to offer protection to whichever circuit is in use.

The distribution system for high voltage is the same as for domestic systems whereby a ring main is used for the power sockets. This ring main comprises a cable which can take the maximum amperage of the system, say 30 amps, connected to each socket in the system in turn. Obviously connections are in parallel to avoid any voltage drop, and the whole circuit is protected by a fuse which would have a 30 amp rating if it was a 30 amp circuit. The circuit is called a ring main because it returns to the main distribution board, giving in effect two alternate paths for the current to the sockets. For a complex electrical installation you could have two ring mains if the load was expected to exceed the normal 30 amp maximum. Each appliance is independently protected by a correctly rated fuse in the plug.

Heavy current users such as cookers, water heaters and air conditioners would be permanently wired in with their own circuits connected through a fuse or circuit breaker in the main distribution panel. The lights, which are low current users, would have their own separate circuit, again protected by a fuse or circuit breaker probably rated at 5 amps. In this way the electrical supply circuit is divided up, with the fuses or circuit breakers giving appropriate protection and the wiring being appropriate to the capacity of the appliances. Lighting circuits are not normally earthed on shore, but on a boat this is a wise precaution, particularly when metal light fittings are in place.

The type of wire used for electrical circuits in the home is not generally suitable for use on boats unless it is very well secured. This wire generally has a single core copper wire inside the insulation so that if it is subject to any movement or vibration it can break through fatigue. Special wiring is produced for use on ships, but it is very expensive; a good compromise is to use a double insulated, good quality flex. Here the copper wires are made up from twisted thin strands which are much more resilient to fatigue. Each core of the three core cables is individually insulated, with a second covering of insulation added to enclose these insulated wires, providing double protection against cable damage. For normal use in a boat PVC (polyvinyl chloride) covered cable is adequate, but if the cable is subject to heat, for instance where it passes through the engine compartment, then the more heat resistant EPR (ethylene propylene rubber) should be used.

The normal domestic variety of plugs, sockets and connection boxes is generally adequate. They will not stand up to damp, but if your boat is damp to any extent you should not really have shore power installed. Any fittings which have to be mounted where they might get damp or wet should be of the fully waterproof variety. As at home, there should not be any high voltage sockets in the toilet or shower compartments, and think carefully before installing high voltage lights in the shower compartment because they will certainly get wet.

Shore power electricity can bring the comforts of home on board, but it can also be dangerous. Keep sockets and other fittings away from hatches or windows where they could get wet. Make sure your installation is sound, check it out at regular intervals and don't take chances.

5

Monitoring and distribution

Now we have the batteries and the method of supplying them with current, so the next stage is to look at how the current can be distributed to the appliances around the boat. The need for the system to be reliable is obvious, but you will also want to be able to monitor what is going on. Is the battery getting an adequate charge? What current is being used by the system and what is the state of the battery? If you know what is happening you will get peace of mind from knowing that the electrical system is working satisfactorily – but just as important, you will hopefully get early warning when something is not right. It is much better for this early warning to come from the monitoring instruments than wait for smoke to billow from the cabin to indicate a problem.

Let's look at the monitoring side first because this is the key to a successful installation. If you know what is happening in the electrical system you will come to understand it better and be able to use it intelligently. Two main instruments are involved here, the ammeter and the voltmeter which measure amps and volts respectively. These have to be installed in the circuits in the correct place in order to give valid information and perform a useful function.

Ammeter

The ammeter measures in amps the amount of current flowing through the system. Chapter 2 explained that battery capacity is measured in ampere/hours, ie the battery can supply so many amps for so many hours, and by multiplying the amps and hours together you have the capacity of the battery. If you keep taking current out of the battery, however, it will eventually end up flat, so the ammeter will give you some idea of how much current you are taking out or putting in to the system.

The ammeter will only show how much current is being taken out of the battery when the engine is stopped – when no current is being fed back in to replace what is being taken out. Similarly, if no current is being taken out of the battery then the ammeter will register the number of amps being fed into it from the alternator, the battery charger or even by solar panels or a wind generator. For much of the time current is flowing both in and out of the battery, so here the ammeter will show the balance between supply and demand. If there is more current flowing out, the ammeter will register on the negative side of the scale, indicating that the battery is steadily losing power. If there is more current coming in than is being used then the ammeter will register on the positive side of the scale and you will be reassured that all is well. By showing the balance of the current flowing in and out of the battery you can obtain an instant picture of its state of health, and any readings on the negative side should be a warning that the battery is being depleted. This will not be a problem in the short term but could be serious if allowed to continue.

Some information about battery charging can be obtained from the charging light, or ignition light as it is often called. This lights up when the ignition is switched on, and once the engine is started it should go out. Car drivers will be familiar with this type of indicator light. When the light goes out after the engine has been started it means that the voltage produced by the alternator is higher than the voltage coming from the battery.

You might wonder why we are talking about voltage here rather than amps which is the measure of current flow. Well, if you think back to the charging circuits you will remember that the regulator only allows the current to flow from the alternator to the battery when the voltage from the alternator is higher than that of the battery. This indicator light is therefore telling you that the current is flowing and the battery is being charged, but it doesn't tell you at what rate it is being charged nor how much current is being taken out.

The indicator light is connected between the D + or the 61 terminal on the alternator and the starter switch live terminal, which in effect is from the battery. It usually comes as part of the engine wiring harness and control panel, and is a relic from the car industry where it is considered adequate as a monitoring device for the electrical system. On a boat it does give an indication that things are working on the charging side, but it does not show whether the charging current is balancing what is being taken out of the battery. The charging light is really no substitute for the ammeter which can give more useful information. An indicator light of this type might be adequate for a small boat with a basic electrical system, but anything larger should have an ammeter fitted into the circuits.

The ammeter has a scale with zero at the centre, the minus scale to the left and the plus scale to the right. If the battery is discharging then the pointer will show the amount on the minus scale, whilst if there is more current going into the battery than being taken out, the pointer will move over to the plus side. The ammeter scale has to be selected to cover the expected charge and discharge rates; a typical ammeter could read from -50 amps through zero to $+50$ amps.

The ammeter is connected in series between alternator and battery so that the current flows through it. This arrangement is fine if the amount of current it has to measure is low, say less than 20 amps, and also if the ammeter is located close to the alternator/battery link so that long leads are not required. However, long leads to the ammeter could cause a voltage drop which would affect the charging system. On most modern installations, a shunt is incorporated in parallel to the

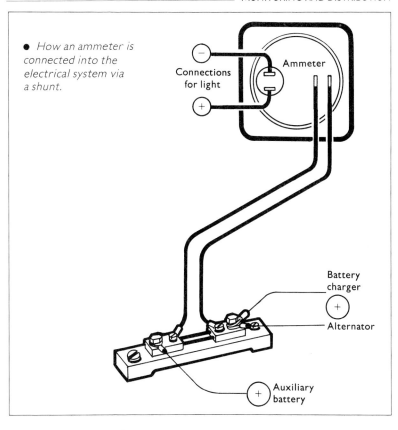

● *How an ammeter is connected into the electrical system via a shunt.*

ammeter to overcome the problems of running long wires in heavy duty cable to the ammeter.

The shunt is simply a fixed resistance device which carries the main flow of current from the alternator to the battery. A fixed proportion of the total current is diverted through the ammeter, which measures the proportion and then corrects for it on the display scale. In this way the ammeter leads only have to handle a small proportion of the main current, which allows it to be placed in the most convenient location without the problem of voltage drop or the need for heavy duty wiring.

One ammeter will only measure the current going into one battery, so if you have a dual battery system you will need separate ammeters for each. However, with such a dual system it is normal to use an indicator light for the starter battery, because here you are only interested in what is going into the battery, the current coming out being too high for the ammeter to measure. If the indicator light goes out then you know that current is flowing from the alternator to the battery and you can be reasonably comfortable that all is well. An ammeter can then be fitted to measure the current flow into and out of the auxiliary battery where things can be more critical.

The ammeter situation can be more difficult when you have alternative means of charging the auxiliary battery, such as a battery charger, solar panels, etc. You will also want to know what these chargers are putting into the battery. Whilst the mains battery charger may have its own ammeter fitted, this will not be readily visible, so it helps if the main ammeter can show this input. This can be achieved by connecting the battery charger, the solar panel, or the wind generator into the alternator side of the ammeter shunt. The diodes in each individual charging system will prevent feedback on the ammeter. However, an ammeter reading from zero to 50 amps may not be sufficiently sensitive to show the small amount of charge generated by a solar panel.

Voltmeter

The voltmeter measures the voltage of the system and is always connected in parallel, measuring the voltage across the two points where it is connected. The main purpose of the voltmeter is to give an indication of the state of the battery charge. For this quite delicate measurements are required so the voltmeter should have a suitably expanded scale over the range which is of interest. For a 12 volt system the scale should range from 8 to 16 volts, whilst for a 24 volt system it should be from 18 to 32 volts.

The reading shown on the voltmeter has to be used in conjunction with the way the electrical system is being used. For instance, if the battery is being charged from the alternator or a battery charger then the reading should be between 13.8 and 14.1 volts, which is the normal voltage supplied to charge a 12 volt battery. The actual voltage will depend on the regulator used. If the voltage goes higher than this it means that the battery is probably fully charged and it will start gassing if the regulator does not cut back the current to a trickle charge – something you should be able to identify on the ammeter.

When the battery is not being charged the voltage will be lower. A fully charged 12 volt battery in good condition should have a voltage of around 12.7 volts, and the voltage will stay between this figure and 11.6 volts whilst it is being discharged. When the reading reaches 11.6 volts the battery can be considered empty of charge and it is time to start putting a charge back in. If the battery continues to be discharged when the voltage reaches this reading then damage could result and any reading below 11 volts should be regarded as entering the area of permanent damage.

The battery voltage will take some time to settle down after it has been charged. It can take an hour or two to drop to the full charge reading of 12.7 volts from the charging voltage, and of course if the battery is used during this time there will be a bigger drop. The same happens in reverse if the battery is used for engine starting because the sudden heavy load of the starter motor can drop the voltage to 8 volts.

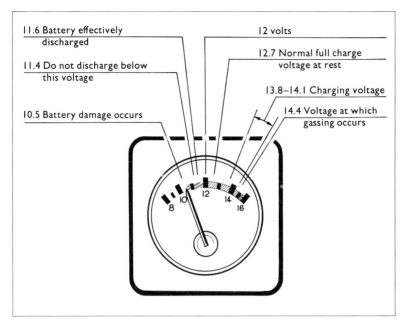

11.6 Battery effectively discharged

11.4 Do not discharge below this voltage

10.5 Battery damage occurs

12 volts

12.7 Normal full charge voltage at rest

13.8–14.1 Charging voltage

14.4 Voltage at which gassing occurs

● *An expanded voltmeter seal which shows the meaning of the battery volt-age readings. The scale is often coloured to warn of the danger areas.*

Once the starter load is disconnected the voltage will rapidly rise to 10 volts, but it could take half an hour to recover to top the 12 volt mark. If the engine has started you won't be aware of the slow recovery because the alternator will be charging the battery, which will then allow the voltmeter to show the charging level of around 14 volts. So you have to know what is taking place when you look at the readings on the voltmeter. Anything over 12 volts can be regarded as comfort-able until the reading reaches over 14 volts, when the battery will be charged and gassing could occur. Anything below 11.6 volts is a warn-ing that you will soon be without any power at all and it is time to replace some charge. With a 24 volt system all these figures will be doubled.

To illustrate just how important this business of voltage is, let's look at engine starting. A fully charged battery will show a voltage of 12.7 volts, but if the voltage drops to only 12 volts it is unlikely that you will be able to persuade the starter motor to turn over the engine. The difference of only 0.7 volts can mean having a running engine and being dead in the water. A DC powered refrigerator may start to have prob-lems if the battery voltage drops to 12.4 volts. With the refrigerator starting to lose efficiency it will start operating continuously to try to maintain temperature, causing a heavier drain on the battery and fur-ther reducing voltage. Electronics are generally less sensitive to volt-

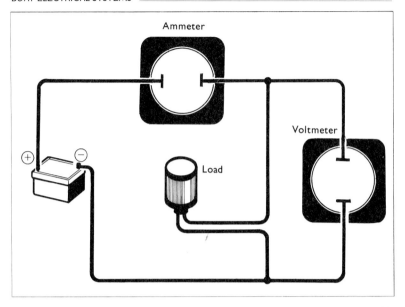

● *How the ammeter is connected in series and the voltmeter is connected in parallel.*

age drop and can tolerate voltages even down to 10 volts, but radios, with their high powered transmitters, do not take kindly to a drop in voltage.

Some voltmeters have colour coded scales to help interpretation of the readings, with red and green colouring to indicate the good and bad areas. However these coloured areas are only a guide and must be used in conjunction with knowledge of what the system is doing. A scale which allows an accurate and sensitive reading of the voltage is a much better proposition.

The normal place to connect the voltmeter is across the main terminals of the distribution panel. This is effectively in parallel with the battery terminals. When deciding where to connect the voltmeter remember that any long cable runs could create a voltage drop unless adequate sized cable is used, and this could give misleading readings.

A portable voltmeter is useful when making an electrical installation. Unsuitable sized wiring, bad connections and long cable runs can all lead to a reduction in voltage by the time the current reaches an appliance. By measuring the voltage at the battery when it is not being charged and then again at the appliance, any voltage drop can be detected; it is then simply a question of finding the cause. We will be looking at this in more detail in Chapter 8.

The voltmeter sometimes goes under the name of battery state monitor. As far as the basic instrument is concerned, they are the same, but the difference will be apparent in the scale. For a straightforward voltmeter the scale will simply read from, say, 8 to 16 volts with no attempt at interpretation. On the battery state monitor the scale is more likely to be divided into zones which give an indication of the battery's state of health but, as already mentioned, you do need to know what is happening within the system to make a valid interpretation.

Distribution boxes

The distribution box is exactly that – a box or panel where the main supply to the auxiliary systems throughout the boat is divided into individual circuits to supply the various items of equipment, and where these circuits are protected by individual fuses or circuit breakers. The reason for dividing up the system in this way is largely to isolate each item of equipment on its own circuit so that a fault in one will not put other items out of action.

How much the electrical system is divided up at this point is largely a matter of personal choice. Obviously you don't need to put each individual cabin light on its own circuit, otherwise the distribution box would have to be unnecessarily large. Equally it would not be sensible to have all the lights on the same circuit otherwise a failure would put all the lights out of action at the same time. This could be particularly the case with the navigation lights, where you could be embarrassed if they all failed together. At least if the masthead lights and the sidelights are on different circuits other craft would still be able to see you whilst you tried to fix things.

Each piece of electronic equipment justifies its own circuit, so that the circuits can be protected by a fuse to match the power requirements of the equipment, and in general all the major items of electrical equipment should have an individual circuit. Each should be protected by a fuse or a circuit breaker and should also have a switch so that only those circuits required need be activated and any faulty circuits can be isolated. A distribution box on a new boat should have facilities for additional circuits to be built in, particularly important these days when a number of extra pieces of electrical equipment may be added. This can rapidly use up the extra circuits; we will look at coping with this situation in Chapter 9.

Because the distribution board is the focus of the auxiliary electrical installation on board it should be located where it is easily accessible, both for operating the switches and for rectifying faults. The main cables which carry the current from the battery to the distribution board should be as short as possible to reduce voltage drop – and remember that these cables are not normally protected by fuses so a very high standard of installation is required. Whilst it is convenient to have the distribution box close to the steering position, particularly if the ammeter and voltmeter are installed on it, it must also be in a position where it will stay dry. The numerous contacts at the back of the box can make this a prime target for corrosion if it gets damp.

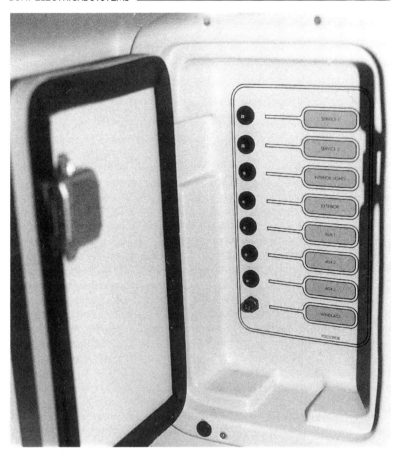

● *A very tidy distribution box with the fuse holders on the left marked with the fuse ratings. Note the board is housed in a watertight compartment to give added protection, but it needs dismantling for access to the wiring at the back.*

Fuses

Fuses comprise a thin metal wire which is designed to melt and break the circuit when the current in the circuit reaches a prescribed level. The amount of current the fuse will handle depends on the cross section of the wire used in the fuse and they are rated in amps. There can be an element of confusion about the rating of fuses because some fuse manufacturers maintain that a 10 amp fuse is designed to 'blow' when the current in the circuit reaches 10 amps, whilst others hold that a 10 amp fuse is designed to carry up to 10 amps, but to 'blow' if the current goes higher. In the latter case the current could reach, say, 12 amps before the fuse blows.

The difference is unlikely to be too serious because neither the fuse nor the circuit it protects should operate to such critical limits. Whilst the fuse wire itself may be manufactured to closely controlled limits, in time weakening of the wire may occur through slight flexing or when securing screws are tightened around it, so it is quite possible for a fuse rating to reduce. If a circuit normally carries around 6 amps then a 10 amp fuse would be appropriate. The fuse rating may have to be raised to, say, 15 amps if there is an electric motor in the circuit in order to allow for the starting surge. If this is the case then the wiring of this circuit should also be upgraded to match even though the surges are transient.

If a fuse blows on a regular basis then it could be that it is too small for the job it has to do – but try to find the reason first before putting in a larger fuse. It could be that additional loads have been added to that particular circuit to make the fuse limit more critical, or it could be caused by an electric motor taking a heavier load because it needs servicing. Try to find the cause before simply putting in a larger fuse and then, before you do, check the circuit to ensure that it can handle the heavier load. (See Chapter 6).

There are various sorts of fuse; those normally used on boats are cartridge fuses. The open fuse which can be replaced with a piece of fuse wire is not particularly satisfactory for boat use, partly because the wire is exposed and open to corrosion, and also because it should be contained in a fireproof box because of the heat and possible sparks caused when it blows. It is certainly less expensive to use fuse wire, but it can be a fiddly job on a tossing boat at night; the cartridge fuse is much easier to handle.

Cartridge fuses come in three different types. Firstly the normal fuse in a glass cartridge where you have to peer closely to see if the wire has broken, second is the powder filled cartridge which is normally used for higher value fuses to reduce sparking and heat, and finally the quick blow type where the fuse wire is tensioned by a spring so that the ends jump apart rapidly when the fuse blows. This latter type is normally used for equipment where even a slight current surge could cause damage to delicate electronics. Both of the other types are used on boats, sometimes in clip holders at the back of the distribution board and sometimes in screw-in holders accessible from the front. There are also fuse holders which can be connected into a wire; these separate fuses can often be found behind the dashboard to protect the ignition circuits.

Circuit breakers

The circuit breaker performs the same function as the fuse, but instead of a wire link that melts, the circuit breaker is rather like a switch which opens the circuit when the current load exceeds a certain limit. There are three different types of circuit breaker, one triggered by heat, one working on a magnetic basis and the third which comes in the form of a combined switch and circuit breaker.

The heat type has a bimetallic strip comprising two metals which expand at a different rate when heated. This causes the strip to bend when it reaches a certain temperature, and this bending is used to open contacts in the circuit when excess current passes through. Normally the strip would heat up slowly with excess current, but this type of breaker has a mechanical device which causes the contacts to snap open to make a clean break and reduce sparking.

The magnetic type will break the circuit when the current in the coils of the breaker reaches a preset limit. This is the most popular type of breaker used today, and whilst earlier designs were liable to open circuits through the pounding of a boat in a seaway, modern designs have overcome this and will only open the circuit through current overload. They provide a reliable means of circuit protection and have the big advantage over fuses that if they do open, the circuit can be quickly completed again by pushing in the breaker. It should not be held in, because if there is a fault this could create overheating or damage in the circuit, and if the breaker will not stay in then it's time to start looking for the fault in the circuit.

This type of magnetic breaker is now often combined with an on-off switch, so that in one fitting you have the control systems for the circuit. It is even possible to get waterproof versions of these combined switch/circuit breakers for mounting at an open steering position. A more sophisticated version combines both magnetic and thermal breakers in one unit so that there is double protection.

Power supplies for electronics

The proliferation of electronic systems has shown that the rather crude electrical supply on boats is not always suitable for delicate electronics. Whilst modern equipment is remarkably tolerant to variations in the supply voltage, there can be a requirement to isolate them from the worst variations in order to give them a reasonable chance of operating successfully.

The main problems arise from power surges when large users of current such as radio transmitter and electric motors such as the anchor windlass, are switched on and off. The starter motor can also be a culprit, although this is not generally a problem as the power is usually taken from a separate battery. Nearby lightning strikes can also cause surges which will upset delicate electronics, and a variety of surge suppressors is now available which can offer a degree of protection.

These surge suppressors are fitted across the terminals of the equipment to be protected, ie in parallel with the equipment. In normal use they pass only a tiny amount of current, but when a surge comes they open a bypass and allow the surge to flow, taking it away from the equipment they are protecting. Whilst the electronic equipment is most in need of such protection, a similar surge suppressor could be fitted across the battery terminals to protect the sensitive alternator,

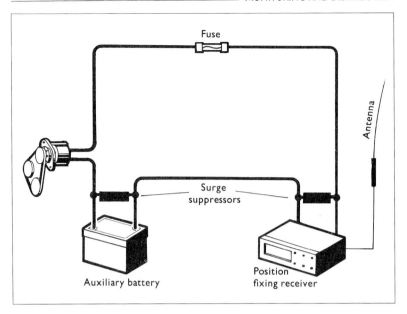

● *A simplified supply circuit showing how surge suppressors are incorporated to protect the battery output or sensitive items of equipment.*

although this is only really necessary if your boat operates in an area where lightning is prevalent.

Emergency power supplies

Some parts of the electrical system on board could be considered vital to the safety of the boat. You could manage without the cabin lights or the refrigerator, but items such as the navigation and compass lights and perhaps the position fixing receiver are much more important. In the event of a fault developing in the electrical circuits, particularly at night. It can be reassuring if you can switch over these vital circuits to an alternative supply and postpone finding the fault until you get back into harbour.

It is up to you what you consider vital, but try to keep the list reasonably short so as not to complicate the wiring system too much. You can then arrange for a separate power supply for this equipment through a secondary distribution board. This should be just like the main board in terms of having breakers and labels for each circuit, and in addition it will have a changeover switch. Under normal conditions, this will be supplied with power from the auxiliary battery in the same way as the main board, and to all intents and purposes, it will be part of the main distribution board, but if there is a failure in the auxiliary battery or its circuits, then the changeover switch could allow you to draw power from the starter battery as an alternative.

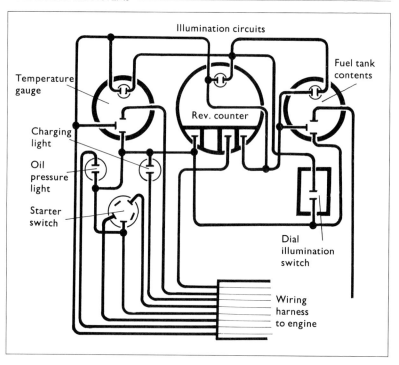

● *Typical dashboard wiring circuit which is usually included as part of the engine wiring harness.*

You could take this emergency power arrangement even further by having separate circuits all the way to each piece of equipment, each of which would need a separate changeover switch. However, if you narrow the list down, this would be an even better way of keeping vital equipment operational because you would then have two completely independent circuits and batteries for the equipment. Certainly as navigation tends to rely more and more on electronics, this is something worth considering.

Engine electrical supplies

These days most marine engines come complete with their own wiring harness. This supplies the link between the engine and its control and monitoring panel on the dashboard and includes such items as the starting switch, oil pressure and water temperature gauges, tachometer and ignition light. It is a tidy way of making this link, but does need a power supply. This usually comes from a source on the engine, such as the solenoid terminal, and separate from the main distribution panel.

Because this is a separate power supply it is often fed from the engine starter battery, which doesn't really create any problems because the power is only required when the engine is running and so you will not be left with a flat battery for engine starting. However, it is just as important for these circuits to be fused as it is for the auxiliary circuits, and in many cases the fuse is in the supply wire and hidden behind the dashboard which can often make it hard to locate. Try to locate this fuse so that you know where to start looking for it in an emergency, because the engine will not start if this blows, and if it blows a petrol engine will stop.

In addition to supplying the starter switch circuits which activate the starter relay, this power also supplies the lighting for the dashboard dials. When the engine manufacturer made up the harness, it was only intended to supply the engine dials but in many cases the boat builder will use this as a convenient point to make a connection for other lighting requirements on the dashboard, such as the compass or additional dials. These may all be connected to a switch or a dimmer. The additional load may necessitate a larger fuse, but the main thing is to be aware that there is a fuse to cover these circuits and know where to find it. It would be much better to have a fixed dashboard mounted fuse or breaker on these circuits which is quite a simple modification to make.

6

Wiring

The wiring on a boat is a vital part of the system and is often the area which tends to suffer from a very casual approach. Even if the original wiring is carried out to a high standard, so often additional wiring will have been installed at a later date which rarely matches the original standards and can be a source of constant trouble. It would be fair to say that the majority of the problems which affect the electrical system on boats stem from the wiring, so setting and achieving the required wiring standards is a vital aspect of establishing a reliable electrical system. It is also an area where things can be improved without incurring a great deal in the way of additional costs.

One of the problems with the wiring in a boat is that faults can gradually become worse and may not manifest themselves for some considerable time. Such is the way of boats; you can be sure that any problems will show up at the most awkward of times, perhaps when you are operating in rough weather, at high speed or sailing close to the limits. This is not surprising because it is at these times that the wiring system is also under most stress, either due to the violent movements of the boat or the salt laden atmosphere. It is these conditions which will start to reveal any incipient weaknesses, and because the deterioration tends to be gradual these times of additional stress can be the point at which the system decides it has had enough and finally gives up.

One reason why the distribution system is divided up into self-contained circuits is because this helps to isolate circuits from each other, so that a problem occurring with one circuit will not affect another. However, it will be obvious that the wiring linking the battery to the distribution board is critical to the whole system and any failure here will affect the whole system. Similarly, some circuits such as those supplying the electronics and the navigation lights can be vital to safety, and even though they are isolated from the other circuits they should come under particularly close scrutiny.

Problems with wiring

When carrying out a survey of the wiring on your boat there are several points to look for. The first is the size of the wiring, because the larger the current which has to be carried, the larger the wire should be. The type of insulation can be just as important depending on where the wiring is installed. However, these details are normally adequately provided for in the original installation; the critical points to look for are the way the wiring is placed in the boat and the way it is secured.

Movement of the wires in the circuitry is one of the major factors which causes electrical problems in a boat; if the wiring is allowed to move then sooner or later there will be problems. Boats move about a great deal in all directions, sometimes violently, so the wiring has to be secured against this movement. What looks perfectly adequate in harbour when the boat is stationary can quickly deteriorate with the boat's movement at sea.

Problems can develop in two areas. If a wire is constantly flexing, then sooner or later the metal in the wire will suffer fatigue and it will break. When and how this happens will depend on the type of wire used; we will look at this aspect later when it comes to selecting the correct type of wire for the job. Chafe is the other enemy, and anywhere where the wiring passes over a sharp edge or is constrained in some way there is the possibility of chafe, which can break down the insulation and increase the possibility of short circuits. Chafe can be a particular problem on metal boats, partly because these tend to have more sharp edges and partly because any breakdown in the insulation on the wire can lead to the current leaking away to earth through the metal of the hull or superstructure.

Both these problems can be particularly hard to locate, which is a good reason to guard against them in the first place. A wire which breaks through fatigue will not necessarily show any defect on the outside because the insulation will probably remain intact. Worse still, the fault may not be continuous because the ends of the broken wire could remain in contact for much of the time, so this can be a very difficult fault to identify and very frustrating because of its intermittent nature. Chafing of the insulation can be just as much a problem, because the area of the insulation suffering from chafe will tend to be the section hidden from view, ie up against the part of the boat doing the damage.

Corrosion can also cause significant problems with the wiring. These problems will be limited to the exposed sections of the wire where it makes connections in junction boxes or with equipment. The damp atmosphere which pervades boats, particularly in winter, can create a ripe breeding ground for electrical corrosion, and particularly when dissimilar metals come into contact, which can often be the case. Here the damp atmosphere can, in effect, become the electrolyte of a miniature battery created by the dissimilar metals which can lead to rapid corrosion.

All these problems are best solved by creating a sound installation at the start. Prevention is better than cure and whether you are upgrading an existing system or starting from scratch, following the basic rules and getting it right at the start is the secret to having an electrical system you can rely on. The difference in cost and effort is quite small in comparison with the peace of mind such a system can bring.

Types of wire

We shall be looking at sizes of wire for a particular job, but first it is necessary to identify the correct type of wire to be used. Here there are two areas of choice; the format of the metal which forms the conducting path for the electricity and the insulation which covers the outside of the metal conductor. Different parts of the boat may require different types of wire and insulation depending on the local environment, and getting this right is the first stage in developing a reliable system.

As far as the metal conductor is concerned, the choice is between a single core wire and a multicore twisted wire. The choice here is quite simple because all boat wiring should use multicore twisted wire. Single core comprising a solid single wire strand is perfectly adequate for use in a house where there is no vibration or movement, but put the same cable on a boat and it could be very susceptible to fatigue breaks.

You will notice that on shore, the connecting cables for all domestic appliances use flexible wires made up from multistrand cores which allows for movement, and the same type of wire should be used on a boat, even if it needs to be well secured. This applies to both the low and high voltage circuits on board.

As far as the insulation is concerned there is a much wider choice. The following are some of the main materials used:

Polyvinyl chloride (PVC)
Synthetic rubber
Ethylene propylene rubber (EPR)
Cross-linked polyethylene (XLPE)
Butyl rubber
Natural rubber

For general boat use where high temperatures are not involved PVC is most widely used and is perfectly adequate for temperatures up to 65°C. It is only in the engine compartment and close to areas such as a heater or cooker that temperatures might exceed this, and for these areas butyl rubber, EPR or XLPE insulation can be used. It should be stressed that temperatures are unlikely to rise to 60°C in the engine compartment except close to the engine, and in these sensitive areas and for the wiring close to cookers or heaters, the manufacturers tend to provide the specialised wiring necessary for the job. So, as a general rule, use PVC cable for all boat requirements unless you have reason to believe that high temperatures might be involved; if so, think about trying to reroute the wiring to avoid the hot spots rather than have to resort to special wire.

There can be confusion between insulation and sheathing. The insulation is the protective material placed directly around the wire to prevent the electrical current leaking out. Sheathing is a second layer

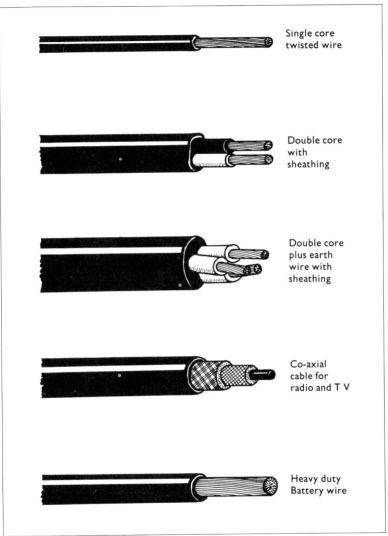

Single core
twisted wire

Double core
with
sheathing

Double core
plus earth
wire with
sheathing

Co-axial
cable for
radio and T V

Heavy duty
Battery wire

● *A selection of the different types of flexible, multistrand wire used for boat wiring.*

put outside the insulation whose function is to provide protection for the insulation so that if the wire is squashed in a hatch or bears against a sharp edge, it may damage the sheathing but hopefully not the insulation.

As a general rule most fixed wiring on a boat comprises a single wire with just a single insulation covering. This in turn is secured in place or protected by a conduit. Double wires with a sheathing tend to be used only where the wire has to survive on its own without protection, such as on the leads which supply a navigation light or the supply to a movable fitting such as a trunnion-mounted electronic instrument. All wiring used for higher voltage shore supply or generator circuits should be of the triple core sheathed type where the third wire is the earth.

Double core sheathed wire for lower voltages comes in two forms, one flat or oval and the other round. The flat or oval cross-section wire can be installed more neatly because it will lie flat against the panel to which it is secured, whilst the round type can be much easier to seal where it passes through a watertight gland.

For a boat rewiring job, then, you might need several different types of wire to do the work efficiently. You can cut corners, but for long term reliability there is no substitute for having the right wire in the right place. Your general philosophy should be to have at least two lines of defence for every conducting wire, which could mean using either sheathed cable or putting the wiring into a conduit.

Size of wire

This is quite a complex area, but as a general rule always use conductor wires which are too large rather than too small for the current they have to carry.

A water pipe will only pass a certain amount of water under a certain pressure and much the same applies to electrical wiring. A wire too small for the job will restrict the flow and this can have two consequences. The first, and potentially the most serious, is that the wire will become hot because of its higher resistance. This means that in severe cases the insulation could melt and cause a short circuit or fire. This is what could happen if there is a short circuit in an instrument not protected by a fuse. Suddenly, the current which wants to flow through the wire is increased, the wire becomes hot, and will not only melt the insulation but in severe cases could also cause the wire itself to act as the fuse and melt.

So heat in the wire is one problem, with the attendant risks involved, but the other aspect which has to be considered is voltage drop. Just as a small pipe will restrict water flow, so a small wire will cause the voltage to drop between the two ends of the wire. This, and the heat created, are linked, because if you have a piece of equipment rated at a certain number of watts, then if the voltage drops in the supply wire more amps will be required to maintain the rated wattage, which starts to overload the wire. So having the right size of wire for the job is important.

The table gives an idea of the capacity of wires of different cross section areas. This rating is given for the more common PVC insulated cable; for the cables which use heat resistant sheathing such as butyl rubber or XLPE a higher capacity is permitted. However, it is best to play it safe and use the PVC rating, and then there will be no problems.

NOMINAL CROSS-SECTION mm²	SINGLE CORE (Amps)	2 CORE (Amps)
1	8	7
1.5	12	10
2.5	17	14
4	22	19
6	29	25
10	40	34
16	54	46
25	71	60
35	87	74
50	105	89
60	120	100
70	135	115

Note that twin core wire has a lower rating than single core because of the close proximity of the two wires. The length of the cable run will also have an effect on the voltage drop because of the added resistance of the cable which has to be overcome. For most of the equipment this is not a severe problem, although for the long cable run up a mast for the navigation light supply you could benefit from using wire one size larger than that given in the table above. The main problems with voltage drop come when supplying equipment which is a large user of electrical power, such as the starter motor or the windlass. One reason why the starter motor battery is placed as close as possible to the starter motor is to keep the cable as short as possible when it can be carrying several hundred amps. Any voltage drop can result in a loss of power at the starter motor.

The anchor windlass supply can be a problem because this motor may require 40 amps or more, and the cable has to be run the length of the boat in many cases. With this level of power to handle, voltage drop could be a serious problem unless the size of cable is adequate for the job. When supplying any piece of equipment containing an electric motor the supply cable should be rated to handle the peak loading on start-up or, with the windlass, when trying to break the anchor out of a hard bottom, rather than the lower continuous loading.

Routeing and securing wiring

It bears repeating that the wires of the electrical circuits must be adequately secured to provide a reliable system. Certainly most boat builders are aware of this fact and tend to work hard to ensure that the electrical system is installed to a high standard. However, short cuts are still taken when wiring is installed behind panels and other hidden areas. These are the places where you don't want trouble because it can be hard to locate the problem. Even on modern boats one still encounters horror stories where wiring is left in a potentially dangerous condition. One example I recall was on a powerboat where wiring had been run across the top of the fuel tank which was located in the bottom of the boat. Single core wiring without protection should not be in such an area, but to make matters worse, when the deck hatch over the tank space was in position the wires were compressed between the metal tank and the hatch, breaking down the insulation. Here were all the components for a serious fire which could be life-threatening, and this was virtually a new boat!

On the subject of fuel tank spaces, try to keep electrical wiring out of this area. If you can't then it should be run through a metal conduit which is earthed, so that if there is damage to the wires the current will flow to earth and not cause sparks in this critical area. In general, it is a good idea to put all wiring into a conduit so that it is well protected. It is now becoming regular practice amongst boatbuilders to install plastic piping in the hull for main cable runs. Some of this piping provides adequate protection for the wires when they are inside the pipe, but if the pipe is too big, then the wires can still move about inside. Probably the greatest weakness of these pipe conduits are the points where the wires enter and leave the pipe. Here there can be sharp edges around which the wire is bent, with the potential for a breakdown in the insulation. There are various types of proprietary conduits on the market, and these are better for the job, partly because they allow access to the wires inside at various points, but they also allow individual wires to exit the conduit at different points. This type of conduit can be used for all the main cable runs through the boat but once outside the conduit the wires must be adequately secured.

The traditional type of cable securing device is a brass strap which is screwed in place over the wire. Today there is a wide selection of securing devices on the market, and the selection of a suitable one will depend partly on the material to which it is being secured and partly on the number and size of the wires being secured. As a general rule, wires should be secured every 15 cm, but the underlying principle should be to prevent any movement in the wire, so closer spacing may be required in some areas.

Many problems can occur at points where wires have to pass through bulkheads or panels. The simple expedient of drilling a hole and passing the wire through is not adequate because it will inevitably encourage the wire insulation to chafe, particularly if the panel vibrates. The hole should be lined with a ferule to give the wire a smooth transit through the panel, and of course if the bulkhead is meant to be a waterproof one then the wire must be passed through a waterproof gland. These are generally necessary for wires passing through the engine compartment bulkhead and for any wiring passing through to the outside of the boat. The latter will generally be for the navigation light circuits, but could also include those for the deck light and horn. By using double core cable with round sheathing the number of waterproof glands required is reduced. Even when the best quality waterproof glands are used on these external fittings there is no point in encouraging water to collect. The gland and wire should be located so the water is not carried down into the gland. This generally means leading the wire up into the gland where possible, and where this is in a vertical panel, putting a dip in the wire just before it enters.

The same approach can also be adopted for internal wiring, where this can be led up into equipment from the bottom wherever practical. There shouldn't be water inside the boat, but a damp atmosphere can lead to condensation which could allow water to run down a wire and into equipment or junction boxes. Taking the wire upwards into these fittings should overcome this problem. Sharp bends are something to be avoided in wiring circuits. A wire which is bent around a sharp

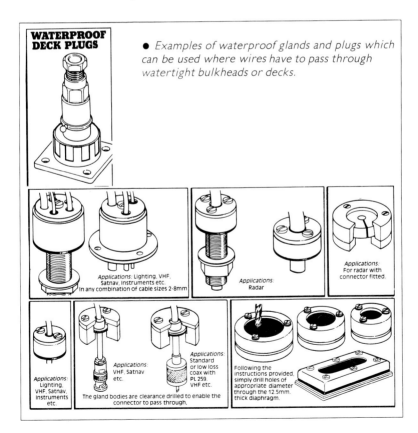

WATERPROOF DECK PLUGS

● *Examples of waterproof glands and plugs which can be used where wires have to pass through watertight bulkheads or decks.*

Applications: Lighting, VHF, Satnav, instruments etc. In any combination of cable sizes 2-8mm

Applications: Radar

Applications: For radar with connector fitted.

Applications: Lighting, VHF, Satnav, instruments etc.

Applications: VHF, Satnav etc.

The gland bodies are clearance drilled to enable the connector to pass through.

Applications: Standard or low loss coax with PL 259, VHF etc.

Following the instructions provided, simply drill holes of appropriate diameter through the 12.5mm thick diaphragm.

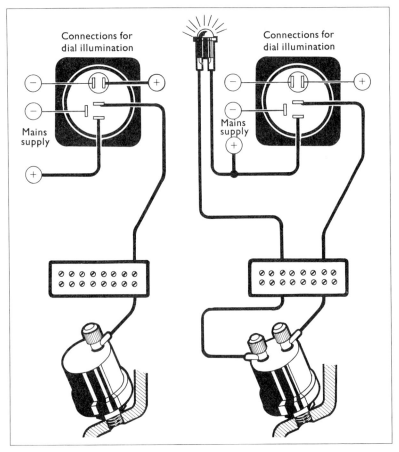

● *How an oil pressure gauge is wired to its sensor on the engine.*

● *The same circuits with a warning light incorporated.*

curve is stretched or distorted in some way, and this can not only reduce the cross-section of the wire at that point but it can also strain the insulation. Both could become trouble spots in the future.

Another potential trouble spot is behind the dashboard. Here there is often a spaghetti-like collection of wiring with a large number of exposed connections. With open steering positions there is a possibility of water seeping in behind the dashboard unless all the gauges are carefully sealed in place. Casual wiring at the back of the dashboard can make it very difficult to trace wires, and the layout and securing of wires in this area needs careful planning to achieve a cohesive system.

The engine compartment can be another problem area, particularly the link between the engine and the surroundings. Flexibly mounted engines means that the wiring also has to be flexible to allow for the engine movement, yet too much movement in the wiring can lead to trouble. In this case the wires can be bundled together so that they help to support each other, or they can often be strapped to a fuel or water pipe to provide the necessary support.

You cannot take too much trouble with the wiring if you want a reliable system. It is largely a matter of commonsense, and whilst it is nice to have wiring tucked away out of sight, do not use this as an excuse for a casual approach to the installation. Try to keep wiring reasonably accessible so that you can check its condition, and then hopefully you will be able to identify problems before they become serious.

Connections

Making the connections in the electrical circuits is a serious business and can be a source of trouble unless they are carried out properly. One of the guiding rules is that the connection should not reduce the cross-section area through which the current can flow. There is little point in having wire of the correct size if you restrict the flow of the current by having poor connections.

The mechanical quality of the connections must also be good. Two wires twisted together will not make a good connection and there is always the risk of it coming apart and causing sparks or short circuits. Even the type of connection where the bare end of the wire is wrapped around a bolt and the connection tightened up with a nut is only satisfactory if there is a lock washer under the nut to stop it vibrating loose. Where the type of multistrand wire recommended for boats is used with this type of connection, or indeed with any screw type connection, there is always the risk of one or two strands not being fully secured with the possibility of touching other nearby connectors.

The best type of connector for use on boats is that where wire is soldered into a connecting lug; the solder makes a very positive connection which is not likely to suffer mechanical failure. If for some reason the heat required for soldering cannot be used, then the second best way is to use pinch connectors, where the case of the connector is compressed around the wire, often with a special tool.

There is a wide choice of soldered and pinch connectors available on the market today. In selecting the right type, the aim should be to make a very positive connection which cannot come loose even under severe vibration or strain. In many cases, the type of connector will be dictated by what is fitted to the equipment being connected, but where there is a choice a closed cable shoe type should be selected in preference to an open shoe. The flat and wire pin or plug types are adequate for boats and are widely used for connections behind the dashboard. Whenever these pinch or soldered connections are used the minimum of live metal should be left exposed to prevent accidental contact with tools or other wiring during inspection or servicing; plastic sleeves are often fitted to cover part of the connection.

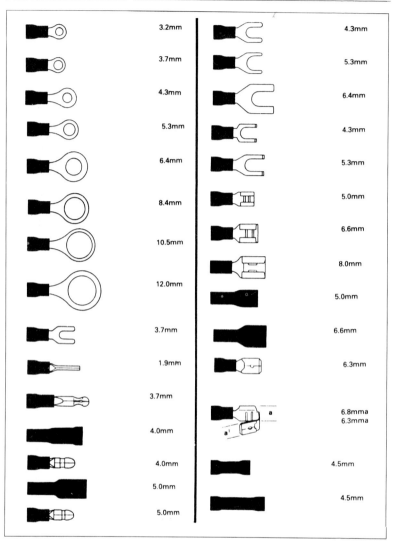

3.2mm	4.3mm
3.7mm	5.3mm
4.3mm	6.4mm
5.3mm	4.3mm
6.4mm	5.3mm
8.4mm	5.0mm
10.5mm	6.6mm
12.0mm	8.0mm
	5.0mm
3.7mm	6.6mm
1.9mm	6.3mm
3.7mm	6.8mma 6.3mma
4.0mm	
4.0mm	4.5mm
5.0mm	4.5mm
5.0mm	

● *The wide variety of connectors which may be found on boat systems. All are suitable except for the two-pronged bayonet type on the top right.*

These plastic sleeves can also help to colour code the wiring system. Coloured wiring can also be used; there is a good range of colours and double colours available now to help identify individual wires. On a car, for instance, the whole wiring harness can be colour coded so that it is much easier to trace faults once you know where a wire begins and ends. The wires can be related directly to a wiring diagram which is

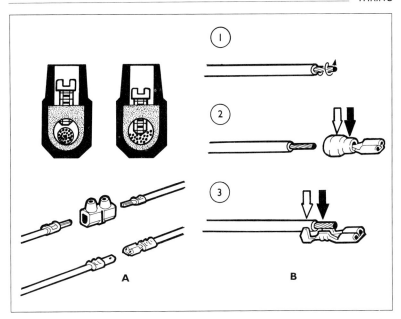

● *Diagram A shows how a soldered wire makes a more positive contact in a screw connector. Below are shown alternative forms of connection.*

● *Diagram B shows the process of fitting a pinch connector, with the first pinch being made at the black arrow to secure the connection, and the second over the insulated part of the wire. The insulating sleeve shown in diagram 2 helps to protect the connection.*

similarly marked, so that you know what each wire does.

The much smaller number of boats produced in common batches does not make interpreting colour coding easy, and this is rarely practised except perhaps on the engine harness and its links to the dashboard. There are no general standards for colour coding, but if you are wiring a boat from scratch then it is a good idea to develop your own, even if it is only a simple system such as red for supply and black for return wires. Certainly some means of identifying the start and finish of each length of wire is a help because it enables the continuity of the wire to be checked in a positive way. If you are undertaking a rewiring job or adding new circuits, then think about labelling each end of the wires so that tracing them during fault finding will be easier.

There should not be any need to make connections directly to the wires in the existing boat circuits. Any new power requirements should in general be taken out as new circuits from the distribution board. However, there are exceptions to this, for instance where additional gauges are inserted into the dashboard or where additional cabin lighting is required. On these connections it is possible to take the power supply from a type of double connection. A flat socket connector can have a branch spade built in so that the branch is taken from the connector. Alternative single input, double output connectors are also available, or with the shoe type two leads can be connected to the same terminal.

General principles

You can have the best electrical equipment in the world, but unless it is connected up properly it will not give good results. Time, money and effort spent on the wiring is never wasted and this part of the system should not be skimped. There are a number of general principles to follow and it is worth summarising them here because of their importance.

Keep wiring out of the bilges and fuel tank spaces if at all possible because faults in these areas could have more serious consequences. Wiring lying in bilge water does not have a fair chance of doing its job properly. Water is the enemy of all electrical systems, so keep all external wiring to a minimum. Where wiring has to pass outside use good quality glands and the best quality of well protected wire.

In all wiring avoid sharp bends and sharp edges where wiring might chafe. All wiring should be secured whether it is out of sight or in full view. Indeed there is more reason to tightly secure out of sight wiring because you won't be checking it regularly. Finally, keep all wires as short as possible to reduce voltage drop and make sure that connections are tight and in good condition.

7

Safety and maintenance

Throughout this book we have mentioned the risks of poor electrical installations on boats and the requirement of high standards to maintain safety. There are two aspects to safety relating to the electrical system, one being the risk of fire which can come from faults in the system itself, and the other the risk from a piece of electrical equipment not working at sea. For instance, if the navigation lights suddenly went out in a busy shipping lane, or the compass light went out in rough seas, the boat could be put at risk very quickly. So the question of safety so far as the electrical system is concerned must be viewed from both sides.

The risk of fire from a short circuit is very real as a personal experience will illustrate. The boat was a 50 foot Dutch-built steel motor cruiser – a good solid boat to be at sea in when the wind was freshening to force 5. The time was 0400 hrs, the time when things often decide to go wrong, and all was fine until the wheelhouse started to fill with thick pungent smoke. The smoke had the characteristic smell of an electrical fire, so the first thought was to switch off the electrical supply at the main switch to stop the cause of the fire.

This had no effect and it took 20 very anxious minutes to rip out panelling and get to the seat of the fire to put it out. From the burned and charred wiring it was difficult to see where the original fault had lain, but by tracing the wiring we found that additional circuits had been fitted which not only bypassed the distribution board and were connected directly to the battery, but which had no fuses incorporated into them. Without doubt, here was the cause of the fire and it explained why switching off the main battery had had no effect. The faulty wiring had been fitted out of sight but loose behind the panelling, and eventually the chafing caused by the rough seas we were in had been enough to cause the short circuit and the fire.

Safety factors

There are many morals to this story, but it does demonstrate how a well planned and well executed electrical system is vital for safety. The trouble is that you can become complacent about the installation because a bad system could last for years before it suddenly decides to let go and create havoc. Safety in electrical systems is dependent on a number of factors which all add up to the complete system.

The example above illustrates the vital role of the battery master switch, which provides a safeguard if things start to go wrong. In this case, the short circuit in the wiring system at fault should have blown the fuse or caused the breaker in the circuit to isolate the fault from the rest of the system. You might lose that particular item of equipment, but at least everything else will keep working. That is the basic principle on which the electrical system works; the only exception to this rule should be an electric bilge pump which you might want to have switched on in its automatic mode to keep the bilges dry when no-one is on board and the battery master switch is off. Even then the bilge pump circuit should be fitted with a fuse so that if a fault occurs the circuit will be automatically isolated.

As far as individual items of equipment are concerned, you can get over the problems of a failure by having duplication. Separate navigation lights could at least leave you with something working if a bulb fails, and of course, there is always the backup of a torch to give you some sort of illumination to indicate your position to other vessels. The torch can also provide a useful backup if the compass light fails. From the point of view of safety it can be a good idea to work through the boat to assess which items of electrical equipment are vital to safety, which ones need a form of backup to guard against failure, and where backup circuits might be relevant.

Starting at the beginning, most boats these days have two batteries and some even more. This can provide a form of redundancy in the electrical system, and in many cases the battery switch can allow you to select which battery is used for a particular job. Even without a selector switch it is possible to change the battery leads over (when the engine is not running) to get extra power for a particular requirement, but if there is a possibility of doing this, either the wires must be long enough to reach both batteries, or the positions of the batteries must be interchangeable.

In trying to plan the electrical system to give you backup equipment, power and circuits, you need to look at all the aspects. In fact the electrical requirements are quite small in a get-you-home situation, even at night. The main requirement is engine starting and running, although with a diesel engine, the engine will run without a power supply once the starter motor has done its job. A navigation receiver could be important, although we did manage quite well before they were introduced, and finally navigation and compass lights. You could add the echo sounder to this list because it could be important as a check if the navigation receiver goes down. Provided you carry spare wire on board and have a charged battery, you should be able to at least get into harbour without any problems.

If you really feel nervous about ending up with flat batteries out at sea, you could carry a spare on board, not connected up, but kept charged when you are in harbour. Such a battery could always be connected up to give a few engine starts and provide enough power for other electrical requirements. However, before you go too far down this route of backup facilities, you might be better off investing in suitable monitoring equipment for the electrical system which would give you early warning that things were going wrong and give you time to do something about it.

When you go to sea, the batteries will be fairly well charged provided you have been using a charger whilst in harbour. Even if you haven't, modern alternators push out a hefty charge which will soon bring batteries up to the mark. Provided you then monitor the ammeter at regular intervals you will soon receive warning that the charging system is not working. At the first signs of any problems on the charging front, switch off all non-essential equipment (which means practically everything) which should leave adequate power in the batteries to get you back to port. On a twin engine boat there is no reason why you should not keep to your original plans even if one engine charging system fails, provided you have a changeover switch, but you will need to keep a close watch on the charging system from that point on.

The other cause of finding yourself with flat batteries at sea is a short circuit in the system. Provided the circuits are adequately protected by fuses this is unlikely to be a serious problem as far as the battery is concerned, but do remember that there are sections of the circuits which do not enjoy fuse protection – the main battery cables to the starter motor and the connecting cables from the battery to the distribution box for example. Any breakdown of the insulation or any damage to these wires could lead to a short circuit which would rapidly exhaust the batteries. You are more likely to be immediately concerned with the fire which would probably result, and only discover the flat battery afterwards, but if you first stop the engine and then go directly for the battery switch to isolate the circuits, then all may not be lost. Even if that battery is exhausted there is always the second to fall back on. With these sections of unprotected wiring the only way to prevent problems occurring is to examine them at regular intervals to discover any incipient problem areas before they go too far.

From all this, you will realise that on a modern boat you would need to have a series of problems and ignore all the warning signs to end up with no electrical power at all. Provided that you watch for the warning signs which will come from both the ammeter and the voltmeter, and understand the significance of their readings, then you will have the early warning to enable you to cope. Knowing how people do not always watch gauges, however, some manufacturers have now brought out alarms which will indicate low charging or battery voltage, but such alarms do not have the subtlety of the information which can be obtained from a gauge, although they will at least alert you to the problem.

At sea, there is much more incentive to keep an eye on what is going on in the electrical department, because your enjoyment and even your safety can depend on it. In harbour the management and use of the electrical system is likely to be a lot more casual, and a flat battery is more likely there than at sea. Most marinas now have a rapid charger

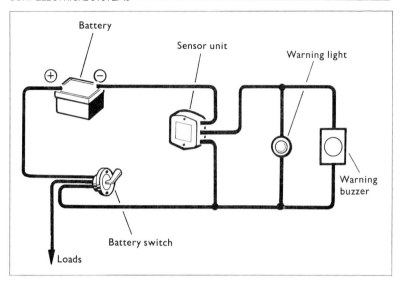

● *How a warning system may be connected into the battery circuits to warn against low voltage.*

which can put enough power into a battery for engine starting in half an hour or so.

The biggest risk from flat batteries is when you are at anchor. Here you have no access to shore facilities for charging, so during a night at anchor you must exercise strict discipline over the electrical power being used and not be tempted to use up the reserves in the engine starting battery. The situation can be similar in a sailboat when the engine has not been in use on a long passage. Again, it is a question of monitoring the batteries to prevent them getting too low and perhaps having some means of auxiliary charging with a wind, water or solar generator to help keep them topped up. The other option is to run the engine at intervals.

Maintenance of charging systems

A modern charging system with its solid state electronics requires very little maintenance. In some ways this is a bad thing because it tempts you to leave it alone until something goes wrong. Unfortunately, this usually occurs at a most inconvenient time, so a little maintenance, even if it just means checking the system, can be justified. The most vulnerable part of the charging system is the driving belt for the alternator. Whilst there is a trend amongst engine manufacturers to use shaft or gear drives for many engine accessories, the alternator remains almost universally belt driven. Perhaps this is because the alternator is not essential to make the engine run, but the vee belt drive of the alternator is subject to breaking and does require adjust-

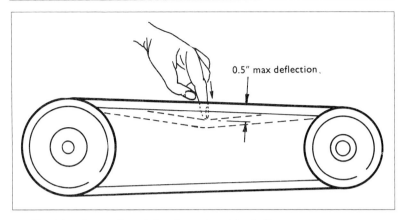

0.5" max deflection.

● *Checking the tension of the alternator drive belt.*

ment. This is a weak point in what is an otherwise reliable system.

The belt drive to the alternator requires regular adjustment to give it the correct tension to drive the alternator efficiently. At full charge the alternator takes a surprising amount of power to drive it, so the belt will be working quite hard. The correct tension, which will be shown in the engine manufacturer's handbook, helps to give the belt a long life and prevents it from slipping on the drive pulley.

To adjust the tension you have to slacken off the adjusting bolts. Whilst you are doing this take the opportunity to either take off the drive belt or at least slacken it right off and look at its condition. Deterioration usually starts on the inside of the belt and you may see cracks in the rubber which can extend part way through the belt. These obviously weaken it and if you find these cracks it is time to renew the belt, on the basis that it is better to do this at a convenient time in harbour than wait until it breaks at sea.

In many cases, renewing the drive belt is simply a matter of taking the old one off, slipping on a new one and then adjusting the tension correctly. However, on some engines it is not as simple as that because a water hose or other connection runs between the drive pulleys and this has to be disconnected first. If this is the case it pays to fit two belts at the same time, taping the second belt out of the way where it is ready for fitting quickly if the drive belt breaks at sea.

Alternator drive belts are comparatively cheap items so it is a good idea to replace them on an annual basis. This will give you peace of mind, but you will still need to check the tension every couple of months or so. At the same time check the connections and the wiring on the charging circuits, the former to make sure that they are all tight and clean and that there is no sign of corrosion, the latter to ensure that there are no signs of chafing or wear and tear. Look particularly at the section of wiring which has to accommodate the movement of the engine on its flexible mounts.

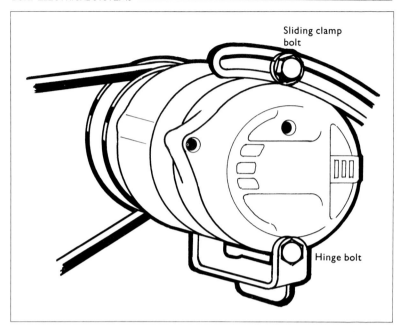

Sliding clamp
bolt

Hinge bolt

● *The tension in the alternator drive belt is adjusted by slackening the hinge and clamp bolts which allows the alternator to swing around the hinge bolt. Tighten well after adjustment.*

Corrosion can be a problem with alternators because these tend to be based on automotive units, and the aluminium body of the alternator can react with nearby brass or steel fittings in a salt-laden atmosphere. The situation can be made worse if there are leaks from the engine cooling system; apart from curing the leak, giving the alternator a spray with silicone grease will help keep corrosion at bay. The same spray can also be used on the wiring connections to reduce the chances of corrosion. The alternator connections should have rubber boots over the exposed metal parts to prevent accidental short circuits when using tools in their vicinity.

Battery maintenance

The requirement for battery maintenance will vary with the type of battery used. The 'no maintenance' type of battery is being used more widely in boats after its acceptance in the automotive market, but anything which is advertised as such tends to be ignored. In a boat it doesn't pay to ignore the battery if you want reliable service from it. Even these no maintenance batteries can benefit from having their tops cleaned at intervals and checking the terminals for tightness and any signs of corrosion.

The main advantage of no maintenance batteries is that they do not require to be topped up with distilled water to maintain the correct level of electrolyte. This can encourage boat builders to install the battery out of the way where access is difficult, and this in turn discourages essential basic maintenance.

Cleaning the top of the battery at intervals helps to prevent any stray currents wandering between the terminals, which can happen if it is damp. Damp is usually the basic cause of corrosion starting at the terminals, and to prevent this it is common practice to smear the terminals with a light grease. Check that the battery remains firmly secured in its stowage, and if it is in a locker check that there is no loose gear lying around which could damage it or short out the terminals. The large cables leading from the battery to the main switch and to the starter motor are particularly critical because they are not fuse protected, so check that the insulation remains intact, that terminals are tight, and that there are no areas where chafing or rubbing might affect the cables.

With the normal type of battery, topping up the electrolyte with distilled water should be a regular task, say once a month, but the frequency will depend on how much the boat is used. It is heavy charging which tends to boil off the water, and if you have a battery charger permanently connected in harbour, you may find that more frequent topping up is required.

Checking the specific gravity of the electrolyte used to be a regular part of battery maintenance, but it has tended to fall out of favour with the advent of modern monitoring systems. However, it is a good discipline to practise, because it will probably give you the first signs that the battery is deteriorating and will soon need replacement. Reading the hydrometer will show the specific gravity of the electrolyte, which in turn will show the state of charge.

SPECIFIC GRAVITY	STATE OF CHARGE
Approx 1.260	100%
Approx 1.230	75%
Approx 1.200	50%
Approx 1.700	25%
Approx 1.140 – 1.110	Flat

If you know that the battery should be fully charged at the time you take the readings of the specific gravity, but the reading is perhaps between the 50 per cent and 70 per cent marks, then you will have warning that the battery has deteriorated and is not holding its charge, so the time for renewing it will be approaching. Of course, the other indication is when the battery fails to turn over the engine on a cold morning; you ignore these warning signs at your peril. On a car, a battery which refuses to turn over the engine tends to be an inconvenience, but at sea it could be a matter of life or death. Give your

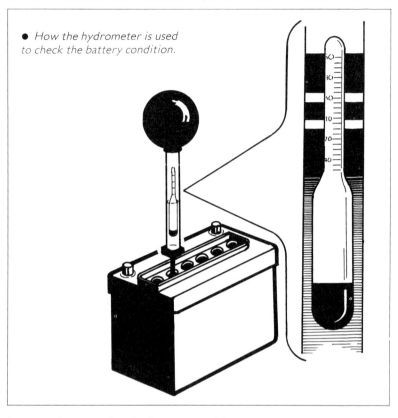

● *How the hydrometer is used to check the battery condition.*

battery the attention it deserves and it will respond with long and reliable service.

Wiring maintenance

Wiring tends to be fitted and then ignored. You react with surprise when an electrical circuit lets you down and yet, if you had bothered to check the system, the warning signs that all was not well were probably plain to see. Like everything else on the boat, the wiring circuits and associated fittings need their share of maintenance if you want reliable performance. An annual check is probably quite adequate, but you need to go through the whole system as far as possible, which is a good reason for installing the wiring and fittings where they are easily accessible.

A quick glance at the wiring will tell you very little. What you need to do during your check is to look at each section of wiring in some detail. Particular areas of interest will be where the wiring passes through a bulkhead or panel or round a sharp bend. These are areas where you can expect to find the insulation being worn down through rubbing against a fixed part of the boat. One of the problems with such an inspection is that the part of the wire which gets the wear and tear is the part which is hidden, so it may not be easy to spot unless you pull the wire away from the contact point. Try not to disturb the wiring any more than you have to, because this could start to develop trouble in the future. Wiring with defective insulation should be replaced. You will quickly learn to look for the likely trouble spots. Apart from where wires pass through bulkheads or round sharp bends, look at the points where wires enter or leave conduit, and where they enter electrical equipment. Look at areas where wires might be left loose behind panels or under floors and pay special attention to wiring to the bilge pump and the anchor windlass (both the bilges and the chain locker being hostile areas for wiring).

Whilst checking the wiring, finish off the job by checking the connections. Connections can be prone to corrosion because they are often the meeting point for dissimilar metals. If you find corrosion, clean it off thoroughly before spraying the exposed metal with a silicone grease spray. Even when you don't find corrosion, use this spray on the connections because it provides a good protective film against future attacks. Also check that all the connections are tight, and look for the tell-tale carbon deposits which can indicate that sparking has taken place around a loose connection.

The distribution box should come under scrutiny at the same time. Once again it will be mainly the connections that you will be looking at, but this is a good time to check the fuses too. Look for signs of corrosion in the fuse holders and make sure that there are adequate spare fuses on board. There is a method of checking the operation of some breakers by means of an overload button, but otherwise there is little you can do other than putting a short circuit into the system to see if they work. It is important to check that there are no signs of corrosion around any of the fittings in the distribution box.

If the boat is fitted with a shore supply circuit or a generator, then pay particular attention to the associated wiring – because of its high voltage it will be less tolerant to any faults in the insulation. The connections between boat and shore should be checked to see that they are dry and clean, and the fittings on the boat should be checked for any signs of corrosion. As far as the generator itself is concerned, maintenance will be covered in the operator's handbook, but keeping it clean and dry will go a long way to encouraging reliable performance.

Maintenance of electrical equipment

The manufacturers' handbooks will cover major aspects, but with items such as light fittings a look inside is a useful part of the annual check. Once again you are mainly checking that the fittings haven't been affected by corrosion, but also look at the wiring inside to make sure that it wasn't nipped when the housing was last closed up. As far as waterproof items such as navigation and deck lights are concerned,

● *Looking down on a sidelight installation. Note the grommet around the point where the wire comes out of the pushpit frame, but there is no grommet where it enters the light holder.*

you should be able to tell from the outside whether there is any water on the inside. There are usually tell-tale stains on the glass from the resulting corrosion.

There are two schools of thought about opening up waterproof fittings. One suggests that these are best left alone because they have been all right up to now, and opening them up might open the way for faults to develop in the future. As far as the navigation lights are concerned, I would be very much in favour of opening up the unit and changing the bulb on an annual basis just to reduce the chance of having to do this at sea. It may be possible to use up any time remaining on the life of the bulb by fitting it in some less critical light fitting. Of course, check for corrosion whilst the unit is open and spray the connections with silicone grease. When reassembling the unit take great care that all the seals are properly in place.

Wiper motors and horns are probably best left alone if they are working well, although an inspection of the outside to make sure that there are no signs of corrosion would be worthwhile. With an open steering position check behind the dashboard display panel to make sure that water hasn't found its way into this critical area. The same goes for the engine control panels on sailboats, which are often located in a vulnerable position on the side of the cockpit well.

With sailboats you should also make a regular check on the electrical fittings at the top of the mast if this is taken out during overhaul. Certainly you will want to renew the bulbs in any masthead lights whilst this is being done, because it can be a major operation trying to change them in an emergency. This can also be a good time to check the wiring which runs up inside the mast because this can suffer chafe from the halyards which run up and down inside. Whilst you are about it, and if it can be done conveniently, it is a good idea to fit spare wires inside the mast so that if there is a problem in the circuits or if you want to add extra fittings you won't have to take the mast down to do the work. Extra wire can be taped in place.

Apart from regular checks on the battery, maintenance work on the electrical system should not take you more than half a day during a year. This is a small price to pay for ensuring that the system remains reliable and is not likely to let you down, but it has the added bonus that by checking through the whole system you will come to know it better. This means that if a problem does develop you will have a much better idea of where and how to look for the fault, a process which is covered in Chapter 8.

Winter lay up

If you lay up your boat for the winter you will need to give the electrical system some attention. The batteries are the most likely part to deteriorate; they should be taken ashore where they can be charged up regularly at home or else the boatyard can be instructed to keep them charged. The batteries could be left in the boat and charged *in situ*, but any leakages in the electrical system could do damage to both batteries and wiring when left unattended for long periods.

It is advisable to slacken off the alternator drive belts for the lay up period, but remember to tighten them again before engine start up. Otherwise all that is necessary is to spray all exposed connections with silicone grease as a precaution against corrosion and take any electrical equipment ashore which you think might suffer if left on board during the lay up. This would probably apply more to domestic equipment powered from the shore supply which might not take kindly to being left in a cold marine atmosphere. Electronic units which are not waterproof could also be taken ashore. Otherwise most of the low voltage fittings should be designed to cope with the winter lay up without suffering.

8

Fault finding

Even in the best installed electrical systems you have to expect failures at some time. The record, in terms of failures in marine electrical systems, is not good, largely because in the past the system was not essential to the operation of the boat. This meant that many of the components used were not well suited to the harsh marine environment and the approach to the installation tended to be casual. All this has now changed, and the on board electrical systems are generally regarded as essential. Boatbuilders and designers have recognised this by raising both the standard of installation and the quality of fittings used, but you must remember that most boats are built to a price, which in turn determines the level of quality. Corners can still be cut in the electrical installation and faults can still occur, so fault finding becomes one of the essential weapons in the boat owner's armoury for survival.

Sometimes faults are visible and there is little need for instruments to help detect them. A wire which has sparked or melted leaves fairly clear signs, provided you can see it, but like many faults the cause and its effect may be in different places. A fuse blowing may be easy to replace, but you have to ask yourself why it blew. Was there a fault somewhere in the system which caused the overload and blew the fuse or was it just a tired fuse unable to handle the normal current load?

You need a logical mind and an understanding of how the system works to be able to track down faults. You also need a few simple tools to help you check components in the system and come up with a solution to the problem with which you are confronted. Without tools, fault finding can be a frustrating experience, and some or all of these tools should be considered essential for seagoing boats.

Fault finding tools

There are several tools which you can use for fault finding; some you can make yourself and others are comparatively inexpensive to buy. Some of these, such as pliers, screwdrivers and spanners, will be part of the standard boat's tool kit, whereas others will be specially designed for electrical work. In this category we might include cross-head screwdrivers, because this type of screw is widely used on electrical fittings.

With regard to special tools, perhaps the most essential item is a multimeter, an electrical instrument which allows you to measure volts, amps or ohms (resistance). This meter has two wire leads which

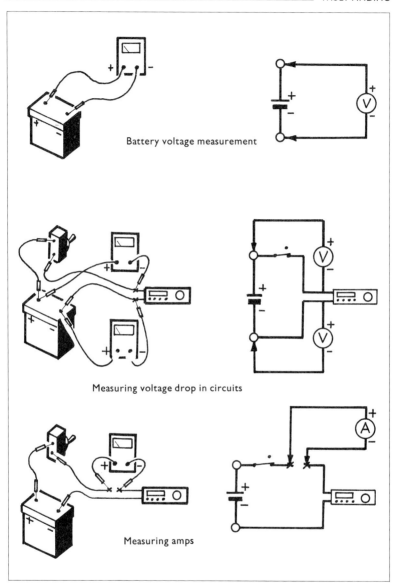

Battery voltage measurement

Measuring voltage drop in circuits

Measuring amps

● *Testing circuits with a multimeter.*

enable you to make contact at the required measuring points, and a selector which enables you to adapt the meter to measure the particular parameter in which you are interested. By measuring amps you can tell how much current is flowing in a particular circuit, whilst by switching to volts you will know the level of the current. Perhaps most useful for fault finding is the ability to measure the resistance. If the resistance is high and the needle on the dial barely twitches, then there is an open circuit, a fact which can be of particular significance if you expect the circuit to be closed and the current flowing. The resistance reading can also be used to check bulbs to see if the filament is intact, fuses to check that they have not blown, and switches to tell if they are opening and closing the circuit.

The multimeter is by far the best instrument for fault finding, but there are less expensive alternatives. The simple neon bulb test probe will tell you if the current is flowing in a particular circuit, which can be a step towards discovering where the problem might lie. There are more sophisticated versions which can be used to check continuity, but if you can afford it, the multimeter is the best type to go for because it allows you to measure virtually all the parameters which will be needed for checking.

One thing the multimeter cannot do is test a circuit to ensure that its insulation is intact. For this you need a Megga tester which generates the high voltage current necessary to put the insulation under pressure. This high voltage current is passed through the circuits, and if there are any weaknesses in the insulation it will break down. This is a valid testing procedure, but it has to be used with care because the high voltage could damage sensitive equipment like electronics. For the sort of basic fault finding you will be carrying out on a boat the Megga tester is not really necessary and is more a tool for the specialist.

In addition to the multimeter or its equivalent, the remainder of the tool kit is very simple. You will need at least one wire, equivalent in length to the longest wire in the boat. This should have a crocodile clip or other connector on each end so that it can be used either as a temporary replacement for a suspect wire, or as an extension for one of the multimeter leads when you want to test the continuity of a long wire. Another quick test device used by electricians is a bulb holder with a bulb of a voltage compatible with your boat's system (12 or 24 volt) with a couple of wire connectors. Simply touch the connectors to appropriate parts of the circuit, and if the bulb lights up then there is power at that point.

Using the tools

Whilst we are on the subject of tools it is worth mentioning just how testing is done. With a bulb tester, you would touch this to the two terminals of, say, a windscreen wiper motor when it is switched on. If the bulb lights up then you know that power is getting to the unit and that the fault lies in the motor itself rather than in the circuits supplying it. You can be quite sure about this unless there is an intermittent break in the circuit, in which case the circuit could be complete when the test is made, but open when subjected to vibration or movement. In this case you can test by connecting the test bulb and then working along the wiring, moving the wire where you can and watching the effect on the bulb.

The neon test lamp works in much the same way, and if it lights up then current is present at the points tested. It is easier and quicker to use when you are trying to isolate a fault, but the test bulb is better for locating intermittent faults. With the neon tester, you can quickly work back through the system, first testing at the unit itself, then perhaps at a junction box, then at the distribution board. In this way the fault can be isolated to a particular part of the circuit or one of the fittings and, once isolated, it is much easier to find a cure. With both the test bulb and the neon test lamp the circuits have to be live when the testing is done.

The multimeter can be used for the same job. To test if current is flowing you would switch it to the appropriate voltage scale. Voltage is measured across the terminals of a fitting and the multimeter not only indicates if there is a current flowing, but you can also infer more from the actual voltage readout. If this voltage is close to that of the battery then the circuits are fine up to that point, but if you receive a significantly lower reading, say 8 or 10 volts on a 12 volt system, then there is some impediment to the current flow. This could be corrosion on a connection or switch or a fatigue break in a wire which still leaves the end in partial contact.

The multimeter can also measure amps. To make this measurement the meter has to be connected into the circuit in series. This is done by disconnecting the positive lead of the circuit, connecting this lead to the meter and then connecting the other meter terminal back from where the positive lead came. This will certainly tell you what current is being consumed by a fitting, which could be useful when you are testing the fitting itself, but amp measurements are rarely used in practical fault finding.

The ability to measure the resistance is a much more useful feature of the multimeter. You are not interested so much in the actual resistance, but whether there is continuity in a fitting or circuit and whether it is open (current cannot flow through it). You can test fuses and bulbs in a positive way by measuring the resistance between each end of the fuse or across the base contacts of a bulb. For a sound fuse or bulb the resistance should be minimal, but when you are testing in this way give the bulb or fuse a tap just in case there is an intermittent break in the filament or wire. It is very reassuring to see the needle of the multimeter flick across to show that a fuse is OK. This is the only positive test for a fuse or bulb because, to the eye, one which has failed can still look fine in some circumstances.

The multimeter can be used in the same way to test circuits. When using resistance measurements for testing, the circuits should be switched off. Connecting the multimeter between the two ends of the circuit to be tested will soon indicate whether continuity exists, and you can also test switches in the circuit by looking at the effect on the

● *Test instruments. On the right is a neon test probe which can indicate if a circuit is live. On the left is a multimeter used to measure all the parameters of an electrical circuit.*

meter needle when the switch is open and closed. A high resistance indicates that the circuit or switch is open, whilst a low or nil resistance indicates that there is continuity.

The significant point when using your testing tools is to know exactly what you are checking. Fault finding in electrical circuits needs a very logical mind to check through each part of a circuit in sequence. When you are taking measurements with the multimeter, test bulb or neon tester, plan the sequence of testing carefully so that the whole of a circuit is covered by the test programme. So often in a boat it is hard to find both ends of a wire for testing once it disappears into conduit or behind panelling. Any fault finding can be greatly assisted by having colour coded wiring or, if you have an existing layout, labelling the wires so that you have a better idea of what you are testing.

Another useful 'tool' is a circuit diagram for the boat's electrical system. You will almost certainly have one for the electrical circuits of the engine in the engine handbook, but not all boatbuilders produce one for the boat itself, or else the diagrams tend to get lost with the passage of time. You can draw up your own diagram which will certainly help you get to know the circuits. Having a circuit diagram can help you plan your strategy of fault finding when you have a problem with the system.

Fault finding

To find a fault in the electrical system you need to proceed in a step-by-step process. Always look for the simple things first. If a navigation light is not working, then first check the fuse covering the circuit and the bulb. You may be able to rule out the fuse straight away if there is more than one light on the same circuit, because if one is still working then the fuse is still intact. This means that it is probably the bulb which is at fault, so that should be the starting point of your hunt for the problem.

It is this sort of logical approach to fault finding which is necessary to achieve results. Other causes of the light not working could be faulty wiring or corrosion in the contacts, but the simple things should be examined first. With something like a navigation light fault, the system is quite simple, and the circuits and fittings are easy to test. When you come to electronics it can be more complex because many items of equipment have a fuse built in, which means that the circuit is protected by two fuses. The fuse in the electronic unit will almost certainly be of a lower value than that protecting the circuits which is located at the distribution board, but it will only blow if the fault is in the unit itself. The distribution board fuse still protects the circuits to the unit.

You may find several of these 'hidden fuses' around the boat. Those for electronic equipment are often hidden inside the unit and it can mean dismantling the case to get to the fuse in order to test it. In other units the fuse may be accessible from the outside but at the back, so if the unit is panel mounted it still involves dismantling. There is no solution to this access problem, although electronic manufacturers may in time realise the error of their ways.

Another place where you may find hidden fuses is behind the dashboard. The circuitry in this area is often supplied as a package by the engine manufacturer who will usually feel the need to include a fuse. This is normally the cartridge type connected into one of the supply leads, and if you are not aware of its existence you can have a frustrating time fault finding because the fuse could be where the fault lies.

If you can't find a fault in the fuse then the next stage is to check whether current is getting through to the fitting. If it is, then the fault will lie in the fitting itself, and you probably won't be able to do much about this at sea apart from checking any internal fuses as mentioned above. If the current is not getting through then work back along the circuits, checking if there is current at the switch and then at the fuse.

In this way you can narrow down the point where the fault lies and then test the continuity of each section of wire by measuring the resistance.

Some test procedures advocate connecting a needle to one end of the multimeter leads so that you can make contact with the conductor wire inside the insulation at intervals along its length in order to pinpoint a break in the wire. There is not much point in this, partly because if there is a break in the wire you will want to renew the whole length, and partly because the pinpricks you make with the needle could be a source of trouble in the future because they weaken the insulation. If you find a wire which appears to have a break then it is much simpler and better to run a new replacement wire alongside the damaged one rather than trying to pinpoint the fault.

Engine circuits

The engine circuits often have warning lights for charging, oil pressure and water temperature. A warning light coming on or not going out can indicate a problem with the engine or it could reveal a fault in the electrical circuits. Once again, a logical approach is necessary, and in the next sections on fault finding we will follow a logical sequence to help you track down the fault quickly, hopefully remedy it, or at least bypass it to allow you to get back to port where you will have time to fix things at leisure or call in expert help.

I   If the starter motor will not turn the engine over, first check the battery condition. If the voltage is around 12.7 volts then there should be enough power available. If not, the first step is to charge the battery, replace it or use jump leads from another. You follow much the same procedure if the battery has enough power to just turn the engine slowly. If you have a twin battery system you may get enough power for starting by paralleling the two batteries with the main switch.

2   If there is adequate power in the battery but the engine doesn't turn, listen for the click of the starter motor solenoid switch when you turn the starter key or press the starter button. If you hear the click then the starter circuits from the dashboard are OK, but there could be a fault in the supply cables to the starter or in the starter motor itself. Tapping the starter with a hammer or spanner could release a jammed pinion which could be the problem, otherwise check the main cables from the battery to the starter for loose connections, breaks or corrosion.

3   If you don't hear the click of the solenoid then the problem will probably be in the starter control circuits. If the dash lights come on when the ignition key is turned then power is getting through to the circuits; if not, then suspect the engine circuit fuse. If these simple checks do not identify the problem then the wiring from the dashboard to the engine will have to be checked.

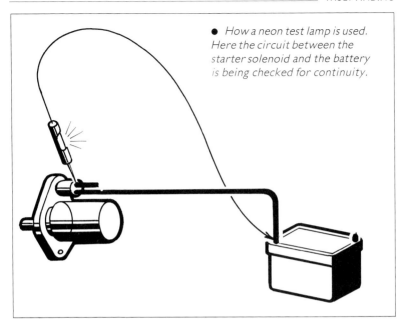

● *How a neon test lamp is used. Here the circuit between the starter solenoid and the battery is being checked for continuity.*

4   If the starter solenoid is clicking and all the circuits seem fine, then the problem is in the starter itself. If you remove the starter motor from the engine, taking care to disconnect the starter battery wire first, you can check the starter to a certain extent by using the multimeter to measure the resistance across the terminals (the case of the motor is usually one terminal). A high resistance will indicate an open circuit in the motor and that it is time for replacement. Detailed testing of a starter motor is a specialist job and you can't do much about repairing one either, although if you are stuck at sea you could check the brushes in the motor to make sure they are not stuck in their holders and check also that the commutator is clean and bright.

Other engine problems

FAULT	TEST	REMEDY
The oil pressure warning light does not come on before starting when the ignition is switched on, but other lights on the dashboard work.	Disconnect lead from the oil pressure sender on the engine and touch it against the engine block.	If the light illuminates then the fault is in the sender which will need replacing. If the light still doesn't illuminate check bulb, wiring and connections.
The oil pressure warning light comes on when the engine is running.	First look for a problem in the oil system (no oil in sump or oil in bilges). Look for a short circuit between the wire from sender and engine block. Also check the sender.	Fit a new section of wire to replace the faulty section if the fault is electrical, or fit a new sender. Otherwise deal with it as an engine lubrication fault.
The water temperature warning light comes on when the engine is running.	A temperature gauge is usually fitted so this can check if there is a high engine temperature. Feel if the engine is hot.	The fault is probably in the engine cooling circuits, but check the wiring to ensure there is not a short circuit.
The charging (ignition) light does not illuminate when the ignition is switched on, but the oil warning light is working.	The first thing to check is the bulb, but it could be a fault in the wiring to the light or a loose connection. This light is also connected to the D + /6l terminal of the alternator.	Check bulb, wiring and connections. Connect a test lamp between D + /6l on alternator and B + . If test lamp doesn't light up check between D + /6l and positive terminal of battery. If the test lamp doesn't light up now there is a fault in the alternator or its control system.
The charging and oil pressure lights do not illuminate when	This means there is no current at the ignition switch	Try the starter; if it works the fault is in the ignition switch

FAULT	TEST	REMEDY
the ignition is switched on.	terminal which supplies the positive connection to the instruments.	or the wiring from the switch to the lights. If the starter doesn't work check the main battery switch is on, the engine fuse is OK and check the wires and connections in these circuits. The fault could also be a flat battery.
The charging light doesn't go out after starting the engine.	There could be a fault in the wiring between the lamp and alternator, but it could also mean that the alternator is not charging. Check first by opening the throttle to increase engine speed.	Check the wire from the charging light to terminal D + /6I on the alternator for a short circuit to earth (eg a bare wire against the engine block). Check that the alternator is turning and adjust the drive belt if it isn't. If either of these doesn't provide a solution, consult an expert.
The charging light flickers.	This indicates intermittent charging.	The fault is probably a slipping drive belt to the alternator which is turning irregularly. Adjust the drive belt.
The charging light glows faintly when the engine is running above idling speed	This could be a high resistance in the circuits to the charging light or an alternator/regulator fault.	Check the connections in the circuits for corrosion and check the resistance of the wire. A fatigue break in this wire could be the cause of high resistance.

If an ammeter is fitted into the circuits this will certainly help when trying to identify some of the problems with charging lights shown in the table. If the ammeter shows a charge then you know the alternator and regulator are working, so the fault will be in the charging light circuits or in the bulb. Make this check with all equipment switched off so you can see the level of charge.

Fault finding on gauges

Problems can occur in the dashboard instrumentation which could at first appear to be an engine problem.

1   If the oil pressure gauge shows no pressure in the engine system then you could be in serious trouble, but it could simply be a fault in the gauge itself or its wiring. The first test will be to check the wiring and connections and to ensure there is current at the instrument when the ignition is switched on. Most gauges have three connections at the back; one for the sensor cable and two for the electrical supply (positive and negative). If you remove the sensor cable then for a temperature gauge the needle should move to the left hand (low) position and to the right for a pressure gauge.

2   Now keep the sensor lead disconnected and use a bridging wire to connect the sensor terminal at the back of the gauge to the negative power supply terminal, keeping the power connected. Now the temperature gauge should move to the right hand position, whilst the pressure gauge will remain on the right as previously. These tests will show that the gauge is working, so the next thing is to test the sensors on the engine.

3   For the temperature gauge switch the multimeter on the resistance range connect between the sensor cable terminal and earth (usually the connection to the engine block). At 40°C this should read about 200 ohms; if the engine is hot (around 120°C) a reading of 30 ohms could be expected. For a pressure gauge the same test is viable, but here the value should be about 10 ohms with the engine stopped and about 200 ohms when the oil system is under pressure. Any readings well outside these values will indicate a faulty temperature or pressure sender.

4   The ammeter will indicate a charge from the alternator and the ammeter can be tested by connecting a 1.5 volt battery across the two terminals with the normal connecting wires removed. The ammeter needle should move, indicating that the gauge is working. If the battery leads are reversed the needle should move in the opposite direction.

Fault finding in the alternator

Probably the biggest mystery to most people when it comes to electrical systems is to identify faults in the alternator. You want to be absolutely sure that the fault in the charging circuits is definitely due to the alternator before buying a replacement unit, and initially the only indication you have that things are not right is that the charging light refuses to go out or the ammeter does not show a charge. You immediately think that the problem lies with the alternator or the associated regulator, but there are many parts of the charging circuits which could prevent the alternator from charging:

1   A faulty battery could affect the charging but you will probably be aware of this and it is not likely to cause a sudden fault.

2   The alternator drive belt may be loose, causing it to slip on the drive pulleys or the belt could be broken.

3   A faulty bulb in the charging lamp could be the culprit. Check the bulb with the multimeter.

4   The wires linking the alternator to the battery, the charging light and the ignition should be checked for breaks, loose connections or other faults. Simple continuity checks should highlight the problem, or it could even be found with a visual check. The alternator can be connected to the battery via the starter solenoid terminal.

Two types of alternator are used on boats; one is battery sensed and the other is machine sensed. You can tell the difference because the battery sensed version has three terminals with wires connected, one being the thick main wire to the battery which normally connects with the main battery cable at the starter motor solenoid. The other two are smaller wires, one to the charging light and one, again, to the starter motor solenoid connection. The machine sensed alternator will have only two wires, a large one to the starter motor solenoid and a smaller one to the charging light. This is the most common type used today, but don't be confused because some high output alternators use twin large output wires to the solenoid terminal. In checking the system, all these wires should be included in the testing.

5   Once you have checked the continuity of the charging circuits and found no problems, then it is time to turn your attention to the alternator itself. A simple check on whether the alternator is charging is to connect your multimeter, switched to a suitable voltage scale, across the auxiliary battery terminals. Switch on a considerable load (say, all the lights and the bilge pump) for about five minutes and then start the engine and run it at about half speed. After a few minutes the battery voltage should read 13.5 volts, provided it is in good condition, which will indicate that the alternator is charging.

6   Another way of testing the alternator is to connect an ammeter between the main alternator output terminal and the large wire to the auxiliary battery. You will need to make very positive connections in this temporary circuit for the ammeter, partly because of the heavy current which can flow from the alternator to the battery, but mainly because a bad connection could result in an

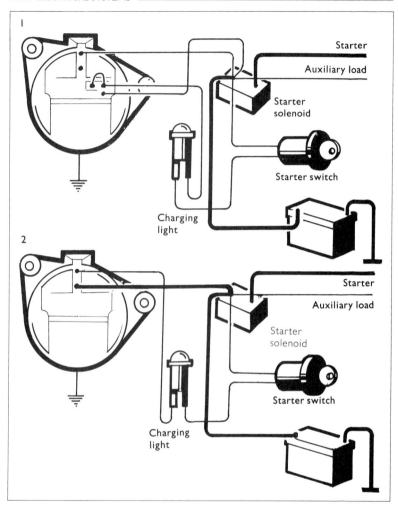

● *Diagram 1 is a typical battery sensed system whilst diagram 2 is a machine sensed system which is used on most modern installations.*

open circuit which could blow the alternator diodes. So before you start the engine first disconnect the battery, then link in the ammeter and then remake the battery connections. Next, switch on an electrical load as mentioned in point **4** before starting the engine and note the alternator output. After the test, disconnect the battery when the engine is stopped before restoring the circuits.

Your multimeter won't be suitable for this test because of the heavy currents involved. If you have an ammeter in the system it should show the same reading as the temporary ammeter, and of course give you a constant indication that the alternator is working –

provided, of course, that all the connections are in order. The temporary ammeter used for this test must be capable of handling the full alternator output. If no charge is indicated then the fault could lie in the regulator if this is a separate unit. When you buy a replacement take both units along so that they can be tested.

There are further tests that can be done on the alternator to check individual components but these involve dismantling the unit. If you are really in a fix, you could open up the alternator to check that the brushes are in order and that the slip rings are clean. However, because it is difficult to buy component parts of alternators and the cost is likely to equate with a full replacement, this is the best option if the alternator is at fault. If you are at sea when the alternator stops charging you should have enough battery power left to get back to port if you use the remaining power economically.

Fault finding in auxiliary circuits

Here a logical approach is essential if you want to find the problem quickly. If you find that a light fitting is not working then a logical sequence of tests can soon narrow down the problem area, and whilst you may not be able to locate the exact fault because it is hidden, either behind insulation or panelling, you will at least be able to identify it closely enough to make a temporary connection across the damaged part. There are two main ways to tackle general fault finding. You can start at the battery end and work towards the fitting which is not working, or you can reverse the procedure. Probably the best way is to do a little of both.

I   Make sure that the electrical power is switched on at the main switch, that the battery actually has power in it and that the correct switch which supplies the circuit in question is closed on the distribution panel. These are the simple solutions and they can be checked without much effort. At this time you could also check the fuse or breaker which covers the circuit, but if this is blown, you still have to find out the cause. It is worth expending a new one to check that the problem was not just a faulty fuse (one advantage of having breaker protection is that you can quickly check to see if it will stay in after it is reset). If the fuse blows a second time or the breaker will not reset, then start looking further for the cause.
2   Now move to the other end of the circuit. If it is a single light which is faulty, then check the bulb. If the bulb is OK, check that the power is getting to the light fitting by using a test light or multimeter at the bulb holder terminals. With other electrical fittings test that there is current coming through the wires at a point as close to the fitting as possible. If there is, then the fault probably lies in the electrical equipment rather than in the circuits,

and you can start checking the equipment itself, looking first for any internal fuses.

3   If the fittings look OK then it is time to start moving back down the line. Ask yourself a few questions like: Is only one fitting not working or are there several? Are these fittings all on the same circuit or connected to the same fuse at the distribution board? Try switching on all the electrical units around the boat to establish just what is working and what is not. If all the ignition or engine related equipment is working but not the auxiliary circuits, then the fault probably lies in the area of the distribution board or its supplies. There may be a main fuse covering all the auxiliary circuits. If a group of lights is not working, try and establish if they are all on the same circuit. The fault will probably lie in the switch or fuse or in some part of the common wiring in that circuit.

4   Before you need to do any dismantling, you should be able to narrow the fault to a section of the circuit. Concentrate on this, checking for loose connections or corrosion at the terminals and then testing the wires for continuity with a test lamp or a multimeter or by running a bypass wire. If you have a wiring diagram of the circuits the task becomes much easier, because you can tick off the parts of the circuits as you test them and it will be easier to see what is left.

Even the type of fault can give you a clue about the type of problem to look for. So far we have been looking at an electrical fitting which doesn't work, which is probably the easiest fault to deal with. Much harder to locate is the intermittent type of fault; a light which flashes or a bilge pump or wipers which do not operate continuously. Then there is the fault which occurs only when it is raining or when there is spray flying about. This type of fault will tax your logical approach a little harder, and you need to think carefully about where the problem could lie, and how to find it.

The intermittent fault is usually due to a bad connection somewhere in the circuit. With a light, it could be a bulb loose in its socket, but it may be a loose connection in the wiring. The hardest type of fault to find is one where a wire has broken inside its insulation and you may only discover this if you run a bypass wire to isolate the faulty section. The problem with intermittent faults is that generally you don't know if you have cured them for some time afterwards, and it can take a fair bit of patience to solve the problem.

Intermittent faults caused by damp conditions can be just as hard to find. They indicate that a part of the electrical circuit which should stay dry is getting wet, with the damp causing either a leakage of current to earth or a minor short circuit, which does not pass enough current to blow the fuse or breaker. Any leakage of current to earth is only likely to be a problem on metal boats where, because the engine forms part of the starter motor circuit, the hull of the boat is also live. Damp getting in to a fitting or at bare connections could cause trouble, but it will usually be indicated by corrosion around the point where the current leak occurs. Do not assume that any current leak of this type will be confined to fittings outside on deck; the trouble is just as likely to start inside the cabin from water leaking through the deck or superstructure and coming into contact with electrical fittings or connections which are not waterproof.

This type of electrical fault, where current is leaking to earth, can have serious consequences in the long term. It will put a steady drain on the battery if left to its own devices without isolating the circuit, but it will also set up corrosion. With a GRP boat such a leakage is not so likely because of the insulating nature of the hull material, but it could be a problem with the wires and fittings on the metal mast. A wooden hull can have damp timbers which conduct current, whilst a metal hull, steel or aluminium, offers a direct path to earth for any leaking current.

To test for these sort of current leaks to earth use a neon test lamp or multimeter. Remove the positive terminal from the battery, switch off all the circuits at or close to the equipment, but leave the battery master switch on. Connect the lamp or meter between the battery positive terminal and the lead which is normally connected to it. There should be no light, indicating no leakage. If the bulb glows faintly then try isolating the circuits from the distribution board one at a time to find the offender, which can be recognised when the light goes out.

You can use the multimeter for this test firstly on the voltage scale; if there is any leak of current this will read 12 volts. If you switch to the ammeter scale you will find out how much current is leaking, but initially use the highest scale and work down to milliamps in case there is a heavy current flowing to earth. You could also use the resistance scale, because with no continuous circuits there should be a high resistance. If you obtain a reading of less than 1000 ohms you must start a search for the fault. With a resistance higher than 1000 ohms the fault will be very hard to find and the current loss will be very small. Even with a newly installed electrical system you will get a small reading, perhaps 10 000 ohms, simply because of the damp atmosphere on a boat. These tests will show there is a leak, but finding it can be a major task. Isolate the circuits to narrow down the search area, and then look for damaged insulating or corrosion around connections.

A point to note when using a multimeter for testing resistance is that if you are touching both terminals with your fingers a small current will flow through your body which could indicate a lower resistance than actually exists.

Fault finding in the mains circuits

The principle behind fault finding on the mains circuits is the same as that used on lower voltage circuits, but you will need different testing equipment and will need to take extra care when dealing with circuits handling currents of 115 or 220 volts. You cannot be casual when making checks on bare wires or connections carrying this sort of voltage, so a general rule is to do as much of the testing as possible with the current switched off. You will need a neon tester specifically designed for the voltage in the circuits being tested; this sort of testing, which checks whether current is getting through to a certain point in the circuit, has to be done with the circuit live. Otherwise isolate the circuits completely by means of the double pole mains switch before starting work.

All the same problems can be found in the mains circuits as in lower voltage circuits. Again, start with the simple things such as checking bulbs, fuses and breakers before moving on to checking the continuity of the wiring. Damp can be a serious problem with these high voltage circuits, and whilst a short circuit caused by damp can lead to blown fuses, an earth leakage can cause longer term problems.

The test for earth leakage is best done with a multimeter which is connected between the positive terminal and an earth point, usually the earth wire of the supply cable or generator. This should show a high reading on the resistance scale when the current is on; any reading below 1000 ohms should have you hunting to find the fault. Some generator installations have an earth indicator bulb permanently connected between the positive and earth wires to give warning of any earth leakage.

This chapter might lead you to believe that with so many potential problems in the electrical circuits there is little chance of getting a reliable system. However, Chapter 9 explains how to install new circuits in a boat, and if you get the installation right, then apart from items such as bulbs and fuses, you should have few problems with the electrical system.

9

Adding extra circuits

Such is the rate of growth in the use of electricity on board boats these days, that extra circuits will almost certainly be required during the lifetime of every boat. It is very tempting to just connect in to the nearest convenient point in the electrical system when you want to add a new piece of equipment, but to adopt this approach is to court trouble. You will end up with overloaded circuits – and simply putting in a larger fuse will not solve the problem because the wiring may not be adequate for the extra current it is being asked to carry. You may also end up with an unhappy mixture of equipment on the same circuits; for example electronic equipment will not take kindly to finding itself in close contact with equipment with electric motors because of the current surges and spikes they can generate.

When planning new circuits for a boat the general rule should be to keep a separate circuit for each item. Certainly all electronic equipment should be on separate circuits from the distribution box, as well as all items which are heavy current users, such as windscreen wipers. Lights, because they are generally low current users, can be on one circuit, but even then it pays to separate them into groups so that if a fuse does blow you do not lose all the lights in one go. The temptation here is to put, say, all the saloon lights on to one circuit, but again, if the fuse blows you are left without any lights in that area. It would be better to separate the lights in the same area into different circuits; you could perhaps put all the starboard lights in the saloon and cockpit on one circuit and the port lights on another.

The same approach could be adopted for the navigation lights; by having them on different circuits you will at least have some lights if a fuse blows and not be blind to other shipping. Here it might be best to keep the two sidelights on one circuit (because one would not be much help without the other) and the masthead and stern light on another circuit. Smaller sailboats tend to put all their eggs in one basket in this respect by having all the lights in a single masthead lantern. It does save battery power, but you will have no lights at all if the fuse blows unless you keep a powerful torch handy.

New circuits are much more likely to be required for additional electronic equipment, or perhaps when you want to install a refrigerator or another bilge pump. The basic circuits for lighting and the other necessities will already be installed, but even so, take a careful look at the overall picture to see what can be done to improve things.

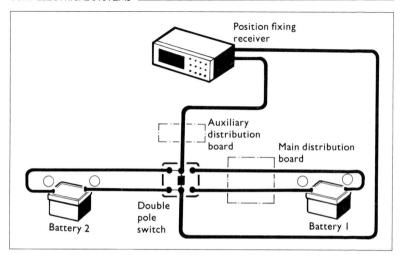

● *One method of wiring an alternative supply circuit to vital equipment. By using the double pole switch, the alternative supply can be switched in if a fault develops in the primary supply.*

Planning the new circuits

Before you start on any installation work, make a plan of what you are going to do. Not only will this avoid mistakes, but it can be filed away with the boat's papers as a reference if there are any problems with the circuits in the future, and it will be important for the guidance of a future owner.

Start by asking a few questions. What is the extra load I am adding to the boat's electrical system? Will the system be able to handle this without major modifications? Are there spare circuits already installed, or at least spare connecting points available in the distribution box?

These questions will give you a starting point for your plan. If you are installing a fridge where there hasn't been one before, you need to be aware that the current load for this unit is quite high, particularly the start up load; the circuit would probably need to be rated at 15 amps. Such a loading could make a considerable increase in the overall electrical load and you might have to think about fitting a larger wire from the battery to the distribution panel. As an alternative, if there is not a spare slot in the distribution box to handle such a load you might install a secondary distribution box with its own wiring back to the battery. With a refrigerator you might consider installing an extra battery as mentioned earlier.

Lighting is unlikely to add significantly to the electrical load, and it may be possible to connect it to an existing circuit; alternatively you may want to take it back to a spare slot in the distribution box. If you

● *The inside of a distribution board showing the spaghetti-like wiring. The two lower sections in the door are the switch/breaker units, whilst at the top are the voltmeter and ammeter.*

are adding a second bilge pump you will not want this on the same circuit as the present one because you won't want the possibility of both failing together. You might want to take the supply for this pump from the main distribution board and not bypass the battery switch, as would be normal with the primary pump so that it is still operational even when the main battery switch is off.

You can see that there are a number of possibilities when it comes to planning new circuits so you do need to decide what you want from them. Whatever you plan, the circuit must include a fuse or a breaker to protect the rest of the installation against a short circuit. This rule applies equally to the bilge pump even if it bypasses the main switch. Once you have decided what you want and drawn a plan of the circuit it is time to work out how you will route the wires through the boat and where the switch and the equipment itself will be located. If you are picking up the power supply from an existing distribution box there will probably be an existing cable route you can follow. Otherwise you will need to find a route which combines easy access with unobtrusive cables. If you have to go back to the battery and route a supply via a new distribution box then the best place to connect in the main supply wires is at the same place as the wires for the main distribution box. This would help to avoid any confusion in the future when it comes to checking the system for faults etc.

Routeing new wiring

The temptation when routeing new wiring is to follow the track of the existing wires. There is a good deal of logic in this, but you may come across difficulties where the old wiring enters a conduit. Trying to get a new wire through the conduit can be a difficult task unless the boatbuilder had the forethought to leave a string with which to pull through a new wire. If there is a string and you use it, do attach another string as well so that there is one left for future use. Another option is to use one of the existing wires to pull through the new wire and a string, then the string can be used to pull the old wire back.

Wiring going through a conduit has the benefit of protection, but another option is to secure the new wire to the outside of it by means of tape or clips. If you adopt this approach use a double insulated double wire, so that it has a degree of protection in its exposed location. For most new wiring it is easier to use a double wire anyway because it means that there is only one cable to route and pass through bulkheads etc, and the wires benefit from the extra protection.

When deciding the route for the wire try to avoid any sharp bends. If the wire does have to pass over a sharp edge, then try to smooth the bend with padding or by rounding the structure at the point where the wire passes. If you can't do this at least give the wire some extra protection at this point. The same goes for places where the wire passes through a panel or bulkhead; apart from the need for a watertight gland in some of these points, make sure the wire is protected at the point where it passes through.

It is a temptation to simply hide the wire behind panelling or the floorboards and think you have completed the job. You might be able to get away with this if you can attach the wire to an existing bundle of wires, but try to imagine what the wire will do once the access hatch or panelling is replaced. Make sure that the wire cannot be trapped or nicked in the replacement process. Finally, keep the new wire away from anything which moves. The main culprit here could be the steering gear, particularly if it is of the wire and pulley type, but you can also come up against this problem behind the dashboard where the wiring and the steering gear are in close proximity. Gear stowed in lockers can also damage electrical wiring if it moves about at sea.

Locating equipment

You will probably have a fair idea where you want to put a new light or new electronic gear, but think about the location from an electrical point of view as well as convenience. It is not a good idea to put an electrical fitting close to a hatch or window, or any opening to the outside, where rain or spray may drop on to the fitting and start corrosion or short circuits.

There are two main problem areas here; the windows of the wheelhouse and the hatches over the engine compartment. The wheelhouse is the area where you are likely to make new additions, so before you decide on a position for a fitting try to picture what will be the effect of water or spray coming in through an open window or door. It doesn't take much corrosive sea water to ruin an electrical fitting.

You can be faced with the same problem in the engine compartment when this is under an open cockpit floor, as can often be the case in both sail and powerboats. Whilst the hatch may be secure and have a drip catch around the edge to stop water passing through, there is always the risk of drips getting through on to equipment underneath. One frequently sees electrical equipment fastened to a bulkhead in the engine compartment where it can be vulnerable to drips getting through the hatch. Even if the hatch is tight and secure, drips can get through as it is opened, and you may need to open it when there is spray or rain in order to fix something below, so try to locate anything electrical clear of the area. If you are installing anything on the outside of the boat, then both it and the wiring leading to it must be water-proof. Even if you are installing a fully waterproof fitting, be kind to it by giving it as much protection as possible. For this type of equipment, only the best will do, so don't skimp on quality if you want the fitting to survive.

Power requirements

We noted earlier how to add up the power requirements of electrical equipment on the boat to establish the power load. When installing new equipment you will obviously be adding to this load so it is impor-tant to ensure that the circuits and fuses can cope. The balance between the fuses and the load on a circuit can be quite fine, and just by adding a new light fitting or even a larger bulb to an existing circuit you could cross the fuse threshold. Its wise to calculate the load on the circuit before making changes.

If the new total load comes close to or exceeds the rating of the fuse, then don't think you can necessarily solve the problem by fitting a larger fuse. Fuse ratings tend to rise in quite large jumps (5, 10 or 20 amps) and if you just exceed, say, the 5 amp rating and fit a 10 amp fuse, the circuit will have less protection because it will need a considerable increase in current before the fuse blows. Also the existing wiring may not be adequate for the higher rated fuse. Rather than change the fuse rating for the circuit, it is better and safer to install a new circuit instead of trying to expand the existing one.

The low power requirements of modern electronics might tempt you to group them all together on one circuit, but this is not good practice. If they are all on the same circuit you will lose them if the fuse blows, which could be serious as we now rely more and more on electronics. Isolating electronics on separate circuits also reduces the possibility of interference. Ultimately, the units are still on the one basic system, but its length helps to provide a cushion against the interference which comes mainly from surges when equipment is switched on and off. This is covered in detail in Chapter 11.

Expanding mains circuits

The chances are that it will be the high voltage mains circuits on board which will be the subject of expansion rather than the low voltage circuits. This is because boat owners are looking to have more of the comforts of home when the boat is in harbour. Whilst the basic principles of installing new circuits remain the same, the higher, more dangerous voltage means that even more care and thought is necessary to avoid risks. This is particularly the case with exposure to rain, spray or even damp. Water and high voltages certainly do not mix, and the location of fittings and wiring must be designed to prevent any contact with water – including the possibility of water running down a wire and into a fitting. A downward loop should be included in all high voltage wiring at the point just before it enters a fitting in order to allow any water on the wire to drip off before it reaches the connection point.

Instead of being wired directly into the equipment itself, as is the case with most low voltage wiring, the mains supply is generally taken via a plug and socket. The sockets are connected up in a ring main which runs round the boat and it is a comparatively simple matter to add a new socket, simply by connecting it. You may need to put a junction box into the ring main and then run wires to the new socket, because if the ring main wire is properly secured there will not be any slack to make the connection directly to the socket.

Any wiring used to expand the ring main circuit must be of the double insulation type. It is normal for this to be three core, with the live and neutral wires fully insulated and the third earth wire sometimes bare, although with the sort of flexible cable normally used on boats the earth is usually insulated as well.

As far as loadings are concerned on the ring main, this will normally be a 30 amp fused circuit, with each socket capable of handling 15 amps if the shore supply can provide this sort of load. In many cases the shore supply fuse will be the limiting factor in what the circuits can handle. Because equipment is plugged in as required the use of the high voltage circuits is more flexible, so you need to be more conscious about what equipment you use and when. With low power equipment such as television sets or radios there is no problem. Even hair dryers and refrigerators are comparatively low power users on these circuits, and you are only likely to have overload problems when you start to plug in such items as an electric kettle when you have the air-conditioning on. If the boat uses electrical power for cooking (other than a microwave oven) there can be heavy loads, but if you are anticipating this level of electrical power then the shore supply must be rated to match, and the heavy power users must be installed on separate circuits from the ring main.

10

Electrical equipment

In this chapter we shall examine how individual items of electrical equipment should be installed and connected. Each item has particular requirements and by examining each in turn we will gain a better idea of the requirements for circuits, fuses, etc, in order to arrive at an installation which will be reliable and give minimum trouble. Let's start with some of the heavy current users because these tend to give the most trouble.

Anchor windlass

Apart from the starter motor, the anchor windlass is probably the most powerful electric motor on board. When running without much load this motor could draw 40 amps or more from the battery on a 12 volt system. When under load or when starting, the load could be up to 140 amps on a 12 volt system. Whilst the windlass is in use for only a short time, it is the circuits required to handle this heavy current which can cause difficulties and which require very careful installation.

It is not just the heavy current which can cause problems. The anchor windlass is located right forward and whilst the hauling section is above deck, the electrics and the motor are below deck where you might think they were well protected. However, the chain locker where the motor is usually located is a damp, gloomy place which has just the right sort of atmosphere to encourage corrosion and short circuits. There is also the problem of the chain thrashing around inside the locker, so the electrical circuits and motor have to be protected from physical damage as well. This need not be a problem if the anchor is dropped slowly using the motor power, but the anchor chain could rush out if the anchor is let go by hand.

Directing the power to the windlass demands long leads from the distribution box to the motor, which highlights the problem of voltage drop. Any significant drop in the voltage will reduce the power of the windlass and cause overheating, so the solution is to fit large cables which are adequate for the motor current. The connections in the system must also be adequate for the current. There really is no room for economy in the windlass circuits if you want the system to work properly.

One alternative to running heavy wiring the length of the boat is to have a separate battery for the windlass. This could be stowed forward, as close as possible to the motor, so that the heavy duty wires are short. This battery could be charged from the alternator via a blocking diode. Such a battery could also be a useful spare in an emergency, but finding a safe location at the bow may be difficult.

When the windlass is controlled from the helm position a relay is used. This avoids running the heavy duty wires to the dashboard; instead you have light wires from the dashboard control which operate the relay or solenoid to switch in the heavy current for the motor (much in the same way as the control for the starter motor, except that a reversing switch is necessary because you want the windlass motor to operate in both directions).

The damp atmosphere in which the windlass motor operates is not kind to electrical equipment. The motor will, hopefully, be a sealed unit which will not be prone to corrosion, but the connections are often exposed and these should be coated with one of the proprietary products which both insulate and keep out the damp. It still pays to have a look at the installation every month or so to check for corrosion before it gets a firm hold. A regular spray with silicone grease will help to keep everything in working order.

Bow thrusters

Electrically powered bow thrusters are becoming increasingly popular on boats to improve close quarters handling. With the motor located low in the bow it has many of the same problems as the windlass motor, and it can take a similar load from the batteries. Both windlass and thruster motors are only used for short periods, so the battery drain is not excessive. The thruster motor and its control system need to be installed and maintained in much the same way as the windlass system.

Air conditioning

Air conditioning systems are becoming popular on boats operating in hot climates. There is a choice of individual units for each compartment or a system built into the boat. There is also a choice of air or water cooling for the system, and on some units the system can also include heating. An owner is likely to opt for the compact semi-portable units if the equipment is being retrofitted, and these now tend to come as bolt-on units which can be fitted to the top of the wheelhouse. They invariably operate from mains voltage, 115 or 230 volts, and can simply be plugged in to the ring main.

Be aware that an air conditioner with heating circuits will be a heavy current user and may need separate circuits wired into the distribution box. Obviously, if you want to use an air conditioner at sea you will need a generator on board. Beware of fitting units designed for homes or motor vehicles on the exterior of boats, as they are rarely designed to be corrosion resistant against seawater.

Trim tabs and power trim

Power trim comes as an integral part of a stern drive or outboard motor, and the wiring is complete apart from connecting in the power supply. Trim tabs tend to be separately installed but the principle is the same, and after installation only the power supply needs connecting. Both of these units operate on the electric/hydraulic principle, with an electric motor driving a hydraulic pump which in turn provides the power to the activating cylinders. Reversing the direction of operation is usually done by means of solenoid valves controlled from the dashboard switch. The electric motor driving the pump can be quite a large current user, particularly with the larger units fitted to high performance craft, and on a 12 volt system they could absorb up to 30 amps. However, these motors are only used intermittently so that the overall load on the battery is small.

The motors are invariably fitted in the engine compartment with stern drive units, but could be in the steering compartment on boats with conventional propulsion. In the latter position they could be subject to damp, and any exposed connections will need protection. In the engine compartment the heat will tend to keep corrosion at bay; here the heat itself could be a problem, so try to keep the motors as far away as possible from hot exhausts.

Autopilots

Although these units are classed as electronic systems as far as the control is concerned, they usually include an electric motor which either drives the steering directly through a chain drive system or is used to power a hydraulic pump which then links into a hydraulic steering system. The electric motors used for autopilots are designed to consume the minimum amount of current, and the units specifically aimed at the sailboat market are very good in this respect. Overall they use very little current (5 watts per hour is the figure quoted for some units), but you have to remember that whilst the overall consumption may be low, the intermittent current can be quite high (up to 15 amps for some of the larger units) so the circuits and fuses must be rated for this level of current.

The dashboard control unit is the focus for the autopilot, but the rest of the autopilot's components tend to be hidden away out of sight. Many of the electrical circuits are included in the manufacturer's specification, but the installation may require the provision of low power circuits between the distribution panel of the autopilot and the relays which control the main drive motor, and of course the supply of power to the autopilot control panel and to the motor itself. Different autopilots will require a different approach, but where one has a motor which switches on and off, then be aware of the higher starting current which is required for the motor. Protect all exposed terminals and connections, particularly when these are located in the steering compartment and allow for cable one size larger when long cable runs are involved. The main power supply must be routed through the distribution box and have its own fuse or circuit breaker.

Bilge pump

Electric bilge pumps are now common on boats of all types. They can be the exception to the rule of taking all supplies through the battery isolating switch, because the bilge pump is one circuit you may want to leave on when the boat is left unattended. Most electric bilge pumps are fitted with an automatic float switch which turns on the pump when the water level in the bilge reaches a prescribed level, hopefully keeping the boat dry when left unattended. I say hopefully, because the average electric bilge pump will not deal with a major leak – say, a cooling water pipe failure – whilst any minor leaks such as a dripping stern tube gland should be dealt with rather than left for the bilge pump to manage. An automatic bilge pump may be necessary on a wooden boat where there is seepage, but a modern GRP boat should not have any leaks, at least of the sort a bilge pump can cope with. However, automatic bilge pumps are often fitted, so if they are to be used in this mode they need to be wired up separately from the main distribution load which is isolated once the battery switch is turned off.

The best place to connect the bilge pump is to the live side of the battery master switch. The circuit will still need protecting against short circuits, so a fuse or circuit breaker of the appropriate rating must be fitted. This fuse is doubly important on this circuit which is left live when the boat is unattended. The rating of a bilge pump will depend on its pumping capacity. A 12 amp 12 volt pump will move around 7500 litres per hour, but such a pump is at the top end of the range, and a small 2 amp 12 volt pump would only handle 1500 litres per hour. The latter type is probably adequate for leaving on when the boat is unattended, and would run for maybe 50 hours before running the battery down. Neither type will be able to cope with a sudden inrush of water.

The bilge pumps are generally submersible, with sealed wiring from the pump. Any connections should be made well above a possible internal water level, and batteries should not be placed too low in the boat where they might be affected by rising water before the pump can rectify it.

Refrigerators

Like most electric motors, the refrigerator motor will use a high current when starting up, after which the current will drop back to the continuous use level. Refrigerators may be rated with the current they will use when the motor is running or they may have the average consumption per hour listed. When you arrive at your boat the refrigerator will have to run continuously for an hour or more before it gets down to its normal operating temperature after which it will run intermittently. A typical small boat refrigerator will consume around 4 to 5 amps per hour, although during the time the motor is running the consumption could be as high as 12 amps, so the circuits must be rated higher than this to cope with the higher starting power needed.

The refrigerator is one of the few motor units on board which runs on a more or less continuous basis. This means that when the engine is stopped it will be one of the main users of current and the most likely cause of a flat battery if care is not taken. Some refrigerators include a device in the control circuitry to warn if the battery voltage is dropping. In some cases this will automatically switch off the refrigerator if this occurs in order to prevent the battery from becoming deeply discharged.

It is possible to buy dual voltage refrigerators so that they can operate on battery power at sea and mains power in harbour. Another option is a refrigerator which can operate from either bottled gas or battery power.

Water pumps

These are installed on boats to provide a water flow when a tap is opened. They operate either with a micro switch which activates the pump when the tap is opened, or by means of a pressure tank which is topped up by the pump when the pressure starts to fall. The intermittent use of these pumps makes their overall consumption low, but the pump motor may use 5 amps on a 12 volt system when it is running. The flicker often seen in the cabin lights when a tap is turned on is an indication of the higher loads on the motor at switch on.

Whilst on the subject of fresh water supplies it is now possible to buy water makers operating from a 12 or 24 volt supply. New technology allows these to operate efficiently to produce around 12 litres per hour with a power consumption of about 8 amps. They can add a useful extra amount of fresh water on a long voyage when the engine is running to keep the batteries charged up.

Heaters

Marine heaters tend to be gas or diesel powered because the electrical loads would be too high unless shore supply or generator power were available. The main requirement with the diesel type of heater is for a power supply for the fan and ignition circuit; here the electrical load is low, probably around 2 amps on a 12 volt system at the higher rated units, and perhaps 0.5 amps on smaller units. Some heaters can incorporate water heating, using diesel or gas. The hot water system is usually controlled and powered by the cold water pressure pump.

Windscreen wipers and horns

These units operate out in the open or are at least partly exposed so there is no substitute for quality here. If possible the wiper motor should be inside where it can be protected from water, but the higher

● *Exterior electrical fittings should be of high quality and require particular care with the wirings and connections to keep water out.*

quality units use a waterproof motor which allows the unit to be mounted on the windscreen of open boats. If the motor is watertight, then the connecting circuitry must be to the same standard.

Wipers come in two types, the normal swing arm type and the rotating arm or screen. The current requirements of both types is around 4 amps on a 12 volt system, with the swing arm wiper being preferred on modern boats because of the larger area it clears. Three wipers may be required for a wheelhouse, making a considerable load in total, but they tend only to be used when the engine is running. With the wiper motor often close to the compass, the magnetic influence has to be considered and the minimum safe compass distance respected.

Horns have a hard life on the outside of the boat and again only the best quality will survive. An electric horn may use 6 amps at 12 volts but the use will be very intermittent and it will only have frequent use in fog, when it becomes an important part of safety equipment. An alternative to the normal electric horn where the wiring and electric components are outside is to have an air horn with the compressor driven by an electric motor. The electrical components can then be inside, protected from water; the power consumption is similar.

Lighting

Various aspects of lighting have been dealt with in earlier chapters but the choice in fittings generally lies between filament bulbs and fluorescent tubes. The latter tend to have a longer life in the marine environment, and give considerably more light for a given power consumption, but not everybody likes the harsh white light they produce. The best compromise is to have a mixture of light fittings, some filament and some fluorescent, so that the lighting can be set for the particular mood. However, standardisation reduces the number of spares required.

● *Watertight plugs and sockets at the base of a mast. The white wires carry the power for the navigation lights whilst the black wire is for VHF antennae.*

Any outside lighting, wherever it is located, must be waterproof. This applies to cockpit lighting in sheltered locations just as much as to the exposed navigation lights. If you use recessed light fittings for outside, then only the fitting needs to be watertight on the outside; it can be linked by standard wiring which is protected on the inside. Fittings such as navigation lights and searchlights can be connected by a watertight deck plug and socket which allows them to be removed easily. The socket should have a waterproof cover to screw in place when the plug has been removed so that water can't get to the live connections in the socket.

Try to keep switches in protected places. It is convenient to have a light switch just inside a door or hatch, but make sure that water can't drip on to it when it is raining or when spray is flying about outside. Even with an enclosed wheelhouse, any switches mounted flat on the dashboard should be waterproof, or at least splashproof, because water can drip onto them from wet oilskins or hands. With an open cockpit all switches and fittings must be watertight; where possible, mount switches vertically where there is less chance of water collecting on the switch.

Electronics

The increasing use of electronics on boats of all sizes has led to increasing concern about providing suitable power supplies for it. This concern can be measured by the number of proprietary 'black boxes' on the market which are offered as a means of providing the correct type of smooth power to the electronic instruments, free from voltage spikes and surges. Spikes and surges are mainly caused by switching equipment on and off, but they also emanate from the charging circuits.

We have already seen how the starting battery can be separated from the auxiliary, which helps to remove the effects of voltage drop created by operating the starter motor. If the electronics were supplied from the same battery the voltage drop could be enough to cause them to temporarily switch off. This usually happens in harbour, so it is not serious from the point of view of safety, but it is irritating when you have just set up the electronics for the start of your voyage.

Separating the starter and auxiliary circuits solves this problem, but it could also occur when heavy power users such as the windlass or the bow thruster are operated. If this is a problem the solution could lie in separating the auxiliary circuits on to different batteries, one for sensitive equipment and one for general purpose use. VHF radios do not normally cause problems in the supply circuits, but powerful HF or MF radios can cause major problems with their high transient power requirements when transmitting. Unlike the windlass or bow thruster, the radio will be used out at sea, so its effect on sensitive electronics should be checked on temporary circuits before finalising its installation.

Apart from the radio, the electronics are used mainly for navigation. The power requirements for logs, echo sounders and navigation receivers are not high, usually in the order of 1 amp or less on a 12 volt system, but navigation receivers and autopilots can be particularly sensitive to the quality of the power supply. Some incorporate smoothing devices in the power input circuitry to improve the quality of the supply but much can be done simply in the layout of the circuitry. Each piece of electronic equipment should have its own power supply with a separate fuse and switch, and as far as possible isolated from circuits supplying electric motors which switch on and off.

The quality of the power supply can be improved by fitting one of the surge suppressors now on the market, but if the quality of the power to the electronics is poor, then think about the option of a separate electronics supply battery. We looked at alternative power supplies for vital electronic equipment in Chapter 5; such an arrangement of circuits could provide a means of switching over if one supply became 'dirty'. Poor quality power supplies can be recognised by internal fuses blowing in the electronics, by unstable displays, and by generally poor performance. Some of these symptoms can result from interference such as radio transmissions and this will be covered in

Chapter 11. Even with a separate battery supplying the electronics there can still be a dirty supply originating from the charging circuits. Special suppressors are available to solve this problem; this too is covered in more detail in Chapter 11.

11

Interference and corrosion

Even though you have taken great care to fit a satisfactory electrical installation in your boat, you can still experience stray currents wandering around the vessel. This is not a reflection on the way the installation has been carried out, but a fact of life which comes from the basic laws of electricity. Dissimilar metals used in the construction of the boat can form a rudimentary battery when immersed in seawater, and unwanted radiated energy from the electrical system can be picked up by sensitive electronic equipment and cause interference. These problems highlight the complex nature of the electrical system and its components on board a boat, and have to be dealt with if you want a system which will operate satisfactorily and not create problems with other parts of the boat.

Radio interference

It is the increase in the use of marine electronics which has really created the problem of radio interference. In the early days of electronics it could be recognised as noise interference on a radio receiver, but today it also affects Loran and Decca Navigator receivers, and of course it can be a problem with on board receivers and hi-fi sets. Radio interference tends to be more of a problem with the lower frequency receivers on board, such as MF and HF radios and Loran and Decca. Fortunately it has far less effect on VHF radios and the new satellite navigation and communication receivers. As the trend is away from lower frequency receivers and towards higher frequency units, radio interference from the boat's electrical system becomes less of a problem. However, with the increase in use of computers on board with their sensitive electronics the problem may reappear in the future.

Radio interference is generated when a current is abruptly varied or interrupted. The current flowing in a conductor generates an electromagnetic field around it, and if the current changes direction or is stopped the electromagnetic field changes, and different usually high transient voltages can be generated. These radiate through the surrounding air and can manifest themselves as interference on the radio or other electronics. The interference can be transmitted to electronic equipment either by the antenna picking up the radiation or an adjacent electric wire being affected by the radiated energy, which can then affect the power supply to sensitive electronics.

Any electrical system on board can generate radio interference. You will hear the click on a radio receiver when a light is switched on or off, but that is an irritation you can live with. The items which can cause

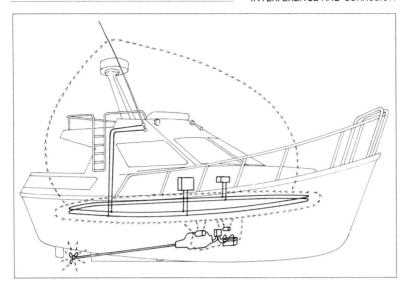

● *Some of the paths radiated and conducted by which interference can travel around a boat.*

more serious problems are those which vary or switch the current continuously – these can include alternators or dynamos, electric motors, voltage and current regulators, blocking diodes, fluorescent lights and convertors. In addition to these electrical components, interference can also be generated from the structure of the boat. This interference is more in the form of static which would normally be earthed. A propeller shaft can generate static which can produce radio interference, and problems could emanate from the rigging where a wire may be making intermittent contact. The ignition system on petrol engines with its spark plugs can also generate interference.

With modern battery charging systems the source of interference is more likely to be the blocking diodes which handle the full current from the alternator. The slip ring and brushes of the alternator handle only a small, perhaps 2 amp, current for the excitation field, but the situation is different with a dynamo where the commutator will carry the full charging current which can spark causing interference. A DC electric motor such as a fan or windscreen wiper motor will have a commutator and this can also be a source of interference.

Modern ignition systems on outboard motors can create radio interference because of the very high voltages involved in the pulsating ignition circuits. The spark plug circuits can also have very high amperages over a very short period of time, perhaps as high as 200 amps. It tends to be the amps rather than the volts which determine the level of interference, so with such a high current radio interference could be a major problem.

Radio interference does diminish with distance from its source, but it can be picked up by other conductors and re-radiated. The guardrails and rigging can do this, and being close to sensitive antennae could pass on the interference. The electrical circuits in the boat can also do this.

Reducing radio interference

It is virtually impossible to eliminate radio interference altogether, but the object is to reduce it to an acceptable level where it doesn't interfere with the electronic equipment on board. The best way is to tackle the problem at source, identify which units are producing the interference, and then try to reduce it as far as possible.

The first step is to switch on radios on the MF frequencies and the Loran or Decca. The latter should be switched to the signal/noise ratio display; an acceptable level for this will be found in the handbook. Have all engines, electrical equipment and lights switched off and check whether interference is present. This can be recognised by noise on the radio (switch frequencies to test it over a wide band) or by a low signal/noise ratio on the Loran or Decca. If interference is present in this condition, then it is external to the boat and you should move to another berth for the test.

Still keeping the radio and Loran or Decca on, switch on each electric motor around the boat in turn. This will enable you to identify any motor which is causing interference. If you find one or more, carry on with the test because there may be other causes as well. Now carry out the same procedure with any fluorescent light fittings on board. Interference from this source can usually be recognised as a high pitched whine, changing pitch over a period of time. With both motors and lights, note any which cause interference for future attention.

Now turn your attention to the engine and charging system. Switch off all the other lights and motors on board and then start the engine, running it up to a speed adequate for the generator to start charging. Note if interference is present on the radio of Loran or Decca. On a twin engined boat carry out this procedure with each engine separately.

If there is no interference then all is well from the point of view of engine and charging system, but if interference is present then the next step is to isolate the alternator and carry out the test again. You can isolate the alternator by removing the drive belt if it is not used to drive the cooling water pump as well. Otherwise, disconnect the main output and field leads from the alternator, marking them for correct reconnection afterwards. If the interference was from the alternator or charging system it should now disappear. A diesel engine should not produce any interference because it has no electrical components, but interference from a petrol engine can be recognised if it remains. Open and close the throttle to note whether the interference rises and falls in step with the opening of the throttle.

Still with the alternator disconnected, take the boat to sea and run the engine both in and out of gear to establish whether there is any interference being generated by the propeller shaft. This will normally rise and fall when the throttle is opened and closed and is only likely to be a problem on boats with inboard engines and conventional propeller shafts.

If you go through these test procedures you will be able to identify the electrical fittings on the boat which are creating the interference. This can save you both time and money, because now you will only need to fit suppression units to those items which are causing interference instead of covering everything.

If the interference is coming from the charging system the best approach is to go back to the manufacturers and ask their advice. Almost certainly they will be able to supply a suppression unit which can be connected into the charging system to reduce interference. By going to the people who made the original equipment you will get a suppressor which is tailor made for your installation, and this should solve the problem. An added bonus with some of the suppression units is that they also provide protection for the alternator if you should inadvertently create an open circuit in the charging system when the alternator is running.

Another step you can take with the charging system is to use sheathed wires to reduce the chance of radiation from the connecting wires. These wires have a braided metal sheath or screen on the outside, and if this is earthed to the alternator casing then it can greatly reduce any interference which may come from the wiring. This should only be necessary when the wiring is close to the electronics, which could be the case when the engine compartment is under the wheelhouse. The logical solution is to route them well away, but in today's crowded wheelhouses, this is not always possible and it is the heavy duty cables supplying radios which are most likely to cause problems and need sheathing. It is possible to buy braided sheathing to fit over cables, but the sheathing must be earthed, usually to the frame of the equipment the wires connect to, although the equipment in turn should also be earthed.

Going back to the charging system, where the various components are separated they should be earthed. The metal casings of the blocking diode and of the alternator help to form a screen against radiation if they are earthed, and this is also a simple cure for electric motors. With motors, an earth will be necessary if you go to more complex suppression systems, so try a simple earth to the casing first. If this doesn't work then a capacitor will need to be fitted between each of the supply leads and earth; one rated at one microfarad will be adequate for most motors on board. You may already find one of these fitted to the alternator for suppression.

The capacitor is connected between the supply lead and earth. Most of the time there will be no current flowing to earth via this route, but

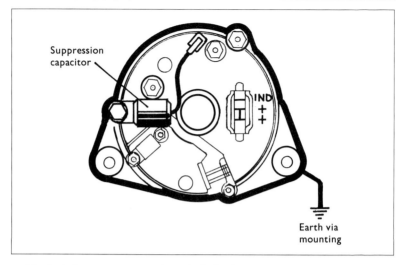

Suppression capacitor

IND

Earth via mounting

● *Typical alternator connections include the capacitor which helps to suppress the interference from the alternator.*

the capacitor allows the peaks and surges of current to flow to earth and dissipate. In this way it helps to smooth out the flow of the current. A choke, which is basically a coil of wire fitted into the supply cables, can have a similar effect, and most of the proprietary surge suppressors or current smoothing units on the market use a combination of chokes and capacitors to smooth out the currents flowing in the circuits and to reduce or smooth the sudden changes which cause radio interference.

It is only by a combination of these units that you can gain the sort of wide band frequency suppression which may be necessary in severe cases of interference. If things are really bad and you cannot solve the problem by the means suggested, then it is time to call in an expert because there is probably something seriously wrong. A logical approach to detecting and solving the problem should bring satisfactory results, so before calling in someone to solve the problem, check that the motor or fitting which seems to be causing the interference is not faulty. Faulty equipment can cause sparking which can be a major source of radio interference.

If the interference is emanating from the ignition system of the engine then there are a number of proprietary systems available on the market. The law in most countries dictates that ignition systems have to be suppressed as far as radio interference is concerned, and you should not have problems on the radio. With Loran or Decca, the interference can be a problem if the antenna is close to the engine, which could happen on small outboard boats. Here the solution is to move the antenna as far away as possible from the engine.

Interference generated by the propeller shaft can be cured by earthing the shaft. A connecting strap fitted over the flange of the propeller shaft connections may do the trick provided the engine is bonded to earth, but remember that this sort of connection will be through the gears and bearings in the gearbox which may not provide an easy path to earth. In severe cases it may be necessary to fit a brush bearing on to a clean part of the propeller shaft and connected to earth in order to get a good connection. Propeller shaft interference is now fortunately rare, particularly as all the stern gear fittings should be bonded to reduce the problems of corrosion which we will look at next.

Corrosion

We have already discussed corrosion on wiring and terminals and the need to keep it in check. This is often caused by the damp atmosphere on a boat and by the use of dissimilar metals at the connection point. If you connect a copper wire to a steel terminal and expose it in a damp atmosphere, then you are in effect creating a mini-battery. Corrosion will develop as a result of this, and unless you keep it in check you will eventually end up with an open circuit and the fitting it connected earlier will not work.

In this sort of situation the corrosion is localised, but a similar effect can be created on a larger scale when dissimilar metals are used on the hull or its fitting. A battery is essentially two dissimilar metals immersed in an electrolyte.

In the case of a boat's lead-acid battery the metals are lead and lead dioxide, with sulphuric acid as the electrolyte. Now on the hull you could get dissimilar metals in the form of a steel or aluminium hull and a bronze propeller. The seawater forms the electrolyte and a current will flow between the two metals. The current itself is small and doesn't cause any major problems, but the corrosion caused by the interaction between the metals can be severe and has to be guarded against.

This type of corrosion is called galvanic corrosion, in contrast to the electrolytic corrosion caused by leakages from the boat's electrical system which we have already dealt with. The way galvanic corrosion works will depend on the metals involved; the following table lists the metals usually found on boats in the order from anodic to cathodic. The closer the metals are to each other in this table, the less will be the reaction between them. Thus gunmetal and manganese bronze could rest comfortably together with no reaction, but put copper and zinc together and you will have real trouble.

When anodes and cathodes are present on the outside of the hull, a current will be generated to flow from the anode to the cathode. It is rather like a battery with the sea water as the electrolyte and in the process, the metals at the top of the table, the anodic metals, will be erroded in favour of those towards the bottom, the cathodic metals. A

ANODIC – ACTIVE

Magnesium alloys
Zinc
Galvanised mild steel
Aluminium alloys
High tensile steel
Mild steel
Wrought iron
Stainless steel – active
Lead
Gunmetal
Manganese bronze
Naval brass
Yellow brass
Aluminium bronze
Silicon bronze
Copper
Monel
Stainless steel – passive

CATHODIC – NOBLE

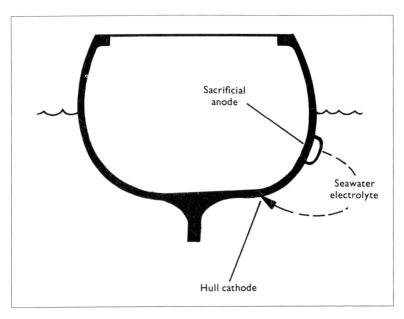

● *The anode protection system works by making the anode from zinc or a zinc/magnesium alloy which is eroded before the other metals in the hull structure.*

● *Anodes around the stern gear. The propeller shaft and A-bracket units are designed for the job, whilst the lozenge-shaped hull unit can be mounted and internally bonded where convenient.*

steel hull will be eroded if the boat is fitted with a bronze propeller, and if there is active stainless steel under water then the problem will be even more severe. The problem is not restricted to steel hulls either, because GRP boats can have stainless steel skin fittings and a steel rudder, mixed with a bronze propeller. On a wooden hull silicone bronze plank fastenings could be a problem with a steel keel shoe or rudder.

It would be safe to say that galvanic corrosion could be a problem on every boat. It can be prevented by fitting pieces of metal to the outside of the hull which are made from zinc or possibly a zinc magnesium alloy. You will see that zinc is near the top of the table, and thus is higher than virtually every other metal. This being the case, it is the metal which will form the anode of the 'seawater battery' and thus is the metal which will be eroded first.

These zinc anodes are normally fitted to the rudder and the areas around the propeller and skin fittings which are the main source of trouble. They can also be bolted around the propeller shaft where this is exposed. Outboards and stern drives have their own special built in anodes. Not only do the anodes have to be through-bolted to the hull, but they also have to be bonded by means of an earth strap or wire to the rudder, the propeller shaft bracket, the stern tube, the engine and to other skin fittings which need protection. With a steel or aluminium hull the bonding may not need to be so extensive because the hull can form part of the link.

When installing the bonding take care with those parts which move, such as the rudder and propeller shaft. It may be necessary to put a

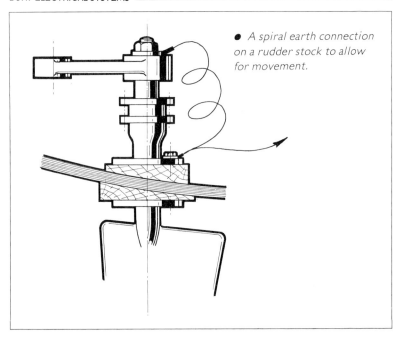

● *A spiral earth connection on a rudder stock to allow for movement.*

bonding strap over a flexible coupling in a propeller shaft, and because you cannot rely on the rudder making contact through the rudder stock a bridging wire is necessary. These wires or bonding strips can form a good earth for any interference suppression equipment or sheathing, and can also help a great deal in reducing propeller shaft generated radio interference. Do not use this bonding system as the earth plate for an MF or HF radio, however. This needs a separate earth plate on the hull which in turn will need cathodic protection.

You can also suffer hull corrosion when lying alongside a steel jetty or even alongside another boat. Ideally the two should be bonded together, but this is the sort of problem that can only be identified by experts; you should only start to get worried if your anodes do not seem to be doing their job properly. The zinc anodes will need renewing at least once a year – more frequently on some boats where there is more active galvanic action. Renew them before they are completely eroded (about 20 per cent left is as far as they ought to go) and do not paint them when you paint the hull because they need to be left bare to make good contact. Do remove marine growth, however, because that restricts the effective area of the bare metal.

Galvanic action and most corrosion which can affect the boat's electrical system will continue day and night whether the boat is in use or not. If you don't use the boat for a month or two then have a quick look round the electrical system to check that corrosion has not started on any connections or fittings. Good quality marine fittings should

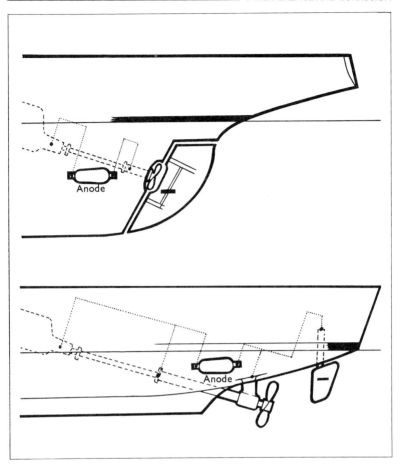

● *Typical anode earth connections on a sailboat and powerboat.*

not show up any problems, but domestic, mobile home or car fittings may not be built to the same corrosion resistant standards. It is not just connections where trouble can start either, but on casings, particularly where aluminium and steel or copper are in close proximity. This can be the case with car or truck type alternators and control boxes. If you can tackle the corrosion in its early stages by treatment with silicone grease or other protective, then it will not become a major problem.

INDEX

EUREKA

2 BATTS @ 75A
        chloride REF 5705

2 @ 678TA (BSX POWERDRIVE
                0800 - 373674)

01523 - 129489